Muck and Mind

Muck and Mind

Encountering Biodynamic Agriculture

~

An Alchemical Journey

Jonathan Michael Code

LINDISFARNE BOOKS | 2014

For my children
Sophia and Michaela,
Young growers and stewards of the Earth,
and my wife
Daniela
Companion throughout.

*... if reason were all, reason
would not exist—the will
to reason accounts for it;
it's not reason that chooses
to live; the seed doesn't swell
in its husk by reason, but loves
itself, obeys light which is
its own thought and argues the leaf
its secret; love articulates
the choice of life in fact; life
chooses life because it is
alive; what lives didn't begin dead,
nor the sun's fire commence in ember ...*

Wendell Berry

Published by LINDISFARNE BOOKS
An imprint of Anthroposophic Press/SteinerBooks
610 Main Street, Great Barrington, Massachusetts
www.steinerbooks.org

Print ISBN: 978-1-58420-181-6
eBook ISBN: 978-1-58420-182-3

Credits:
William Stafford, "In the All-Verbs Navaho World" from *Even in Quiet Places.*
Copyright © 1996 by The Estate of William Stafford. Reprinted with permission of The Per-
missions Company, Inc., on behalf of Confluence Press, www.confluence.com.

William Stafford, "The Way It Is" from *Ask Me: 100 Essential Poems.*
Copyright © 1998 by The Estate of William Stafford. Reprinted with permission of The Per-
missions Company, Inc., on behalf of Graywolf Press, Minneapolis, Minnesota,
www.graywolfpress.org.

Contents

Introduction

The seeds for this book were sown for me as a child. It was my fortune then to experience a close and regular immersion in the forests and lakes of Eastern Ontario. As a toddler, my world extended to the immediate bounds of the pine cabin my parents built and some hundreds of meters beyond. 'Far away' was a sandy beach, down a woodland path patrolled by chipmunks, past boulders and tree stumps, through undergrowth and overgrowth, all easily visible from the cottage door for the watchful adult eye.

As a boy, the boundaries of this wooded world grew to encompass the reach of a row boat—to Blueberry Island, Seagull Island, my Grandfather's cottage, and the (then) distant Indian Bay below my uncle's cabin, across the lake.

As a young man, a further expansion opened up the reaches of Frontenac Provincial Park—portages took us to neighboring lakes where any number of adventures awaited; we weathered thunderstorms under upturned canoes on the rocky shores of Labelle or Big Salmon lakes, found craggy lake-side cliffs high enough to jump off, but too high to tell of to mothers or fathers upon the return. We camped out on islands in the days when tents were tent-shaped and the rain got in through the seams.

In winter, we set out into the distant wintry reaches of the Park, through a foot-thick silence of snow, under a boundless envelope of blue sky—silent but for the swish of skis and the odd 'caw' from a solitary crow out on its daily scavenge.

Over time, with provisions stowed in the bottom of the boat and the timeless reach of summer ahead, the stretch of the world grew by paddle and foot. Trips now extended beyond the Park, to the farm of a close friend several days paddle away, though still only a whisker-distance on the great map of Ontario's lakes and waterways.

And so, seasons spent in the company of beavers and loons provided one entry into a sensible, sense-filled land that fostered for me a profound experience of rooting in the world, with an ever expanding awareness of its complexity and intricacy.

In contrast to these weeks or months spent by the lake, I had an education much like many of my peers. This schooling seemed to consist in a gradual, though strangely well-orchestrated, *removal* from the sensible world into an increasingly abstract and compartmentalized array of unrelated disciplines and departments. The world engaged through this route gradually made less and less sense, was *sensed* less and less.

My love for the so called 'natural world,' fostered by regular encounters with the mixed flora and fauna of Frontenac Provincial Park, awoke in me an interest in natural science, and a thought that a future in Zoology or Biology might be before me.

However, any formal exposure to these approaches to the study of the *living world* (for that is, after all what they seemed to advertise) left me feeling that something was desperately wrong with the way in which these studies were undertaken. The *life* all too quickly drained out of the subject matter presented, and my enthusiasm went with it.

After thirteen years of education, and faced with the general momentum of my peer group which seemed to move inexorably toward several more years of higher education, I abandoned ship.

Faust's words aptly describe my turn of mind at the time:

I pry at Nature's door in vain.
The web of thought is all in slashes,
all knowledge is turned to dust and ashes.[1]

---

1. Translation by Walter Arndt, Norton Critical Edition.

Steering my path away from the hallowed halls of learning, I made instead for travels and explorations around the globe.

These travels were launched for me through a placement with Canada World Youth on an organic farm in New Brunswick, one of Canada's Maritime provinces. Here I encountered a different connection to the world of plant and animal. Questions of preservation or protection were now coupled with considerations of productivity. Economies of scale tussled with economies of sale, ecological benefit versus the bottom line. This was an eye-opening (and muscle straining) time, an awakening to what lay behind-the-scenes of the neatly arrayed supermarket shelves in nearby Moncton.

From this first encounter with the toil and soil of farming life, there followed several years of involvement in agriculture, as well as ever more encounters with the ecological issues rearing their heads in many (if not most) of the places I visited and worked.

Organics offered a rich realm for exploring the interface between the human need for sustenance and the selective rearing of plants and animals that this entailed.

Permaculture offered the proposal that a meeting between 'wild' and 'cultivated' could be achieved through conscious and sensitive design.

Weaving between all encounters were those with ecological activism and the polarized stances that emerged between 'hands-on' and 'hands-off' approaches to our encounters with nature.

There was, for me, through all these years of both working and walking the earth, a lingering 'pea under the mattress,' an itch that I could not scratch, a sense that in all of these perspectives there was—for myself at least—a deeper issue underlying them all.

This feeling arose from the impression that by developing a knowledge of 'dust and ashes,' we had been left high and dry, cast out of reciprocity and mutuality to get on with the manipulation of matter or the cultivation of the Great Me.

In gaining our independent Self we had, it struck me, lost a fundamental sense for the relationship between the whole and the parts, our part in the whole. We were left with any number of ways of trying to bring parts back into some semblance of coherence, but too often stumbled over our own attempts.

My travels eventually led me to the Sacramento Valley in California. Here I encountered for the first time, at a small college in Fair Oaks, the scientific and artistic genius of Johann Wolfgang von Goethe and the many contributions toward social renewal arising from the work and research of Rudolf Steiner. Developed under the title 'Goethean Studies,'[2] the potency of this year was not in a solely theoretical encounter with the contributions of these (and other) innovators in the sciences and arts, but in the experiential and deeply engaging manner in which the course was structured.

Each day began with *consciousness studies*, and a deeply penetrating process of enquiry which recognized that the investigation of the life of consciousness lay at the root of all subsequent research.

This first session of the day was followed by courses in natural science, with a phenomenological and morphological approach. Botany, color, osteology, meteorology ... these were studied along with the, initially surprising, inclusion of sessions dedicated to the alchemical world view.

This intensive course of study, a profound movement of attention between the 'inner work' of the first session and the 'outer work' of the second, ended with a focus on the arts. Painting, drawing, movement, speech and drama—these were opportunities not only for exploring different artistic *techniques* for the sake of artistic expression, but were experienced as integral aspects of a program that sought to weave together the often distinct disciplines of the sciences and the arts.

The impact of this brief year of study cannot be easily described, for it marked a true turning point, a transition between all that had come before, and all that would follow. It hinged on the encounter with a remarkable teacher, friend, and mentor as well as on an opening of grand vistas for further study and research. Echoes of that year in Fair Oaks continue to resound to this day into my present work.

∞

2. Subsequently renamed 'Consciousness Studies,' though still under the direction of its founder and main contributor Dennis Klocek. Dennis' extensive work and range of contributions toward renewal in science, art, and consciousness studies can be found on his website.

It is now many years after my first summer on Northern Arrow Farm in New Brunswick, and a whole new set of circumstances unfolds around us.

A technological world proliferates at a breath-taking speed with ever more 'opportunities' for us to explore. Faust, could he access it, would find in these new technologies much to satisfy his wish that "magic shrouds unpenetrated with every miracle be rife!" It is a world full of potential undreamed of by previous ages.

These technological innovations that have sprung up in my life-time now extend into the realm of *life*—into the many ways in which living organisms are being engineered through a bio-technology that presents itself as the purveyor and guardian of our future crops, medi-cines, and even of our as-yet unborn children.

We can now manipulate life, even create new organisms where— and here is the crux of the matter—we have yet to *understand* them.

The question has not gone away... not for me at least: Are we 'set down here'[3] for greed or guardianship? What is our relation to lamb and loon? Our responsibility? How are we to place ourselves in a time when the significance of both time and *place* are being reduced to nano events, inaccessible to most of us behind screen and wire?

The book that follows is an out-growth of these questions. It emerges from forays into farm and forest, into the halls of science and a search for 'sense.' It is rooted in the domain of agriculture, for it's central pursuit concerns questions deeply connected to work on the land and the provision of sustenance. We are, after all, *consumers*... we rely on the land and its abundance for our nourishment, and as such we rely on those growers and herdsmen who daily do the work of putting food on our tables. I hope that this book will be a contribution to those who tend crops and herds on behalf of us all.

Arising as it does out of my formative years spent by lake and forest, and a sense of reciprocity to the sustaining waters and living creatures of such places, I hope that this book will also contribute to considera-

---

3. " 'Seem like we're just set down here,' a woman said to me recently, 'and don't nobody know why.'" Annie Dillard, *Pilgrim at Tinker Creek*.

tions of how we might be sensitive (and sensible) participants in their mutual unfolding.

Not least, I hope that this book will be of interest to those who are concerned with questions about possibilities for the cultivation of *ways of knowing* beyond those of 'dust and ashes,' which still seem to predominate in the consciousness of our time.

Above all I hope this offering provides food for thought, for thoughtful inter-action with the *living* world in which we are set down.

1

Beginnings

The Way It Is
"There's a thread you follow..."

Setting the Scene

"... the interests of agriculture are bound up with the broadest spheres of human life ... there is practically no field of human endeavor that does not relate to agriculture in some way. Seen from whatever perspective you choose, agriculture touches on every single aspect of human life."

Rudolf Steiner, *Agriculture*

Journal entry: Stroud, Gloucestershire. April 6, 2011

Sun in Pisces, Moon in Aries (both ascending)
Started pulverizing quartz crystals at 11 am
ground on plate glass in full sun
took 3 hrs to grind enough to fill a cow horn
Filled horn with water from 501 stirring (April, 4)
a good day to do silica prep
will bury on Friday at Vale Head Farm.

2 pm, April 9, 2011
Vale Head Farm
Kinver,
West Midlands, UK

I make my way to the top of a paddock that slopes up gently toward the north. Along it's upper boundary, the paddock's edge is marked by a broken, haphazard array of stones and a straggling vanguard of gorse. Out over this gently sloping ground of grass and low herb, old gnarled beech trees reach out from the edge of the woods with wayward, sinuous limbs.

It is hot—unseasonably hot and dry... and bright...

I have chosen this particular paddock on this particular farm for several reasons.

Firstly, this farm sits in the Bridgenorth Sandstone Formation near the small village of Kinver in the English Midlands. It is an area known for its red sandstone, and the rusty colored earth is everywhere visible in outcrops and exposed fields and—underfoot—is noticeably powdery and light. The Kinver rock-houses are a mere half-hour's walk to the east...attractions for tourists but, not so long ago, houses for locals, hand-carved out of the red sandstone bluffs.

The siliceous nature of the soil...the sandstone finely ground under the farm fields... the relative 'dryness' of this soil type—these are the main reasons for my decision to come all this way to Vale Head farm from the Cotswolds in the south.

A second reason for choosing this site is that Vale Head farm is managed as a Biodynamic holding and, having been in conversion for some years now, is already a vibrant mixed farm that emanates a strong sense of the stewardship practiced by its farmer, Ed Berger, and his team.

The quality of care that is evident throughout the farm is a crucial component for someone like myself who is learning about Biodynamics through the burying of horns! For this is why I am here; I have come to dig a hole and bury a cow horn packed with finely ground quartz crystals, and—having made my way to a spot on the curving, south-facing brow of the paddock—I push the spade I am carrying into the earth.

I have no trouble digging down through the soft, friable, sandy soil.

As I dig, I am struck by the thought that, from the outside, this must seem a rather eccentric activity—driving two hours north to dig a hole in a farmer's field and bury a cow horn packed with ground quartz crystals. A furtive glance around

*me, however, reveals only a few bemused Shetland sheep as witnesses to my work.
Digging down, my spade hits smooth, egg-shaped quartz pebbles of various sizes
and soon these are spilling out of the loose sandy soil—river washed stones? here?
in the rolling hills of the Midlands?—a puzzle for the mind to toy with.*

*Keeping aside a small pile of these pebbles, I dig a square hole two feet deep. I
then take up the cow horn that three days ago I filled with finely powdered quartz
crystals, and with only moderate ceremony, I place the horn, tip up, in the bottom
of the hole. I cover the horn first with a layer of the quartz river pebbles—so that
in six months time it is these that the spade strikes first and not the horn—and
then I back-fill the hole.*

*Anticipating a return trip in the autumn, when I will be coming back to find
this spot and dig up the horn once again, I mark the spot with a knot in a piece of
bailer twine, tie the twine to a gorse bush on the uphill side of the hole and—for
good measure—place a sandstone rock over the exact spot just below the level of
the turf.*

*Walking away toward the farm buildings, I am filled with mixed thoughts,
sensations, and images: sandy soil and sun… quartz crystal ground to powder…
filled horn underground… light and warmth… the smell of over-dry earth…*

*Over the next months, although my work and travels take me far and wide,
I am indelibly connected to this small patch of land in the Midlands and my
mind often strays to imagine that single horn, packed with ground quartz, under
the turf in the corner of the paddock at Vale Head Farm, a summer spent underground in sandy soil surrounded by river-rounded pebbles…*

∞

Culture and Agriculture

I would like to place at the outset of this book the following proposal.

I propose that in these still young years of the twenty-first century we stand—globally—in a particularly poignant moment with regards to one of the most essential activities upon which all cultures
and races rely for their daily life and long-term survival. Amidst all the
pressing concerns faced on the political stage or in the economic domain, this realm of which I speak is of central importance because it is

the very foundation for the others, and in it there can be found clear indicators for the health and well being of society generally.

This is the realm of agriculture.

Our inter-actions with soil, with plants and animals, the nature of our *husbandry* (or lack of it), is of pressing concern, for it is in this key interface with the realms from which we draw our daily bread that symptoms of much larger dynamics are revealed. The farmer, essayist, and poet Wendell Berry writes:

> *From the biblical point of view, the earth and our earthly livelihood are conditional gifts. We may possess the land given to us, that we are given to, only by remembering our intimate kinship with it. The condition of the people is indistinguishable ultimately from the condition of the land. Work that destroys the land, diminishing its ability to support life, is a great evil for which sooner or later the punishment is homelessness, hunger and thirst. For some, the context of this thinking has shifted from religion to science, but the understanding of the land as a conditional gift has not changed.*
>
> (Berry, 2013)

Berry's remarkable life-long advocacy of land stewardship finds resonance in a statement made by Wolf D. Storl in his book *Culture and Horticulture*: "It might be claimed that a healthy agriculture is the basis of a healthy culture and a healthy culture implies a healthy agriculture."

Both Berry and Storl are indicating in the above passages that seemingly 'mundane' questions of food—its sources and sinks—lie at the very root, the foundation, of culture itself—its sources and sinks!

We are (some of us at least) privileged to experience an accessibility and relative affordability of food that would seem to make any proposal that there is something wrong with our agriculture seem far fetched. And what of our cultural life? It could be argued that we have never before seen such great cultural achievements as those that we are realizing today in our sciences, technologies, intellectual, and artistic lives. These are contributing in ways never before seen to innovation, communication, and articulation of the cultural life of peoples around the planet.

The obvious follow-on from Storl's statement, however, would be to pause and ask: is our culture really *healthy*? Is our agriculture *healthy*?

As a step toward my own responses to these questions I invite you to consider the following two practical examples of 'solutions' that have arisen in the agricultural domain. The very fact that these innovations have arisen, in one instance with some considerable investment in economic terms as well as in time and human resource, is of course an indicator that issues of ill health *have indeed* arisen within the agriculture realm, and that solutions are needed.

The following examples, taken from current agricultural developments, will serve throughout the pages you now hold before you as lenses through which I will explore the question of *health* in our current agricultural practices. Furthermore, they will provide a mirror, or reflector, for the cultural activity out of which they have arisen. In this way an enquiry into the health of the latter is also explored.

What I hope is that, to begin with, you listen not only to the details of the proposed ameliorations (for this is not initially an enquiry into the suitability of these) but to the kind of approaches taken.

In the first example we find a solution developed to address the problems of pollution arising from intensive hog rearing and, in the second example, a solution for a loss of the vitality in crops and animals as experienced first hand by farmers in the beginning of the twentieth century.

What do these examples evoke for you? What thoughts? Feelings? Impressions?

Example 1

The Enviropig (from the University of Guelph website):

> The Enviropig™ was developed by the introduction of a transgene construct composed of the promoter segment of the murine parotid secretory protein gene and the Escherichia coli phytase gene (Golovan et al 2001) into a fertilized porcine embryo by pronuclear microinjection, and this embryo along with other embryos was surgically implanted into the reproductive tract of an oestrous syn-

chronized sow. After a 114 day gestation period, the sow farrowed and piglets born were checked for the presence of the transgene and for phytase enzyme activity in the saliva. When the mature genetically modified pig was crossed with a conventional pig, approximately half of the pigs contained the phytase transgene. This showed that the transgene was stably inserted into one of the chromosomes of the pigs and was inherited in a Mendelian fashion.[4]

Example 2

Preparation 505 (from *Agriculture*, by Rudolf Steiner)

For this purpose we collect the oak bark that can be easily obtained; we do not need a great deal. Then we chop it up until it is of crumb-like consistency, put it into a skull from any one of our domestic animals—it hardly matters which one—and finally close up the skull, preferably with a piece of bone. Next we place the skull in a relatively shallow hole in the ground, cover it with loose peat, and set up some kind of a pipe or gutter so that as much rainwater as possible flows into the hole. You might even put the skull into a rain-barrel where water can constantly flow in and out. Then add some kind of plant matter that will decay, so that the oak bark in its bony container lies in this organic muck for the whole winter, or better still for the whole autumn and winter. Water from melting snow will do just as well as rainwater. When this material is added to your manure pile, it will truly provide the forces to prevent or arrest harmful plant diseases. (Steiner, 1993, p.101)

---

4. The following statement appeared on the Wikipedia site regarding the Enviropig on 10/22/14: "Ontario Pork ended its support for the Enviropig program in April 2012. The University of Guelph killed the pigs, from the 10th generation of the project, in June 2012 after it couldn't find a new partner to fund the project. However, the genetic material will be stored at the Canadian Agricultural Genetics Repository Program." Although the Enviropig has not found its way into the human food chain, the possibility of its development still exists as long as the genetic material remains.

The Enviropig, a creation of 21st century genetic engineering, was developed to address issues of pollution arising from intensive pig farming operations and the phosphate rich porcine effluents produced in the process. For some, it will evoke impressions of the great pinnacles that science has reached, taking us to the very brink of the laws of life and the potential for the creation of organisms that would not—could not—exist without human intervention.

For others this first example will strike a discord, a potentially visceral reaction that we have—in creating organisms by-design (and patenting them in the process)—overstepped the boundaries of our place in the world, and, far from standing on a pinnacle of brilliance, we have descended to the depths of depravity and created an aberration—a Frankenpig.

The Oak Bark Preparation, on the other hand, may evoke an equally broad range of responses. Some will experience a sympathetic acceptance of the process and product proposed, though perhaps without a thorough understanding of the principles standing behind the various elements which give rise to its creation. Others will have a different response, a downright rejection of this and other biodynamic preparations based on the opinion that we are presented here with pure 'muck and magic,' a throw back to a time long passed.

The Enviropig, it might be argued, demonstrates the clear, rational thinking, so carefully cultivated over the past few hundred years, of scientific research; the Oak Bark preparation… an incomprehensible departure from the rigor of good science.

Whatever response is evoked, both are 'solutions' proposed to address imbalances in the agricultural realm, with significant attention being placed on creating products using innovative, problem-solving, synthetical types of thinking. The striking contrast in the two approaches, which both seek to bring agricultural issues back toward a state of *health* are, on the one hand, indications of the type of problems that farmers face in contemporary agricultural settings; on the other hand, they may also be clear indicators of deeper issues—not just agricultural, but *cultural*. The diagnosis of an unhealthy agriculture may point not only to problems with agricultural practices or approaches, but to a need for attention to be given to the cultural soil out of which those agricultural approaches have grown and developed. *"Seen from whatever perspective you choose, agriculture touches on every single aspect of human life."*

∞

The book that follows arises from over twenty five years of study and engagement with questions and considerations arising from an involvement with land stewardship (as a WWOOFer,[5] gardener, teacher, researcher, and student) and my encounters with 'solutions' such as those given above.

Rather than embarking on a lengthy argument to make a case either for or against genetic engineering or biodynamics I will say from the outset that I have deep reservations about the former and an ongoing curiosity with the latter. The reasons for this stance will unfold in due course.

As it stands, there is ample literature already in print to support (or critique) either of these approaches to developing and maintaining food for our future.[6] The present work is aimed less at questions of suitability of technique, or practical application of methods (or implications

---

5. WWOOF is the acronym for World Wide Opportunities on Organic Farms. "WWOOF organizations connect people who want to live and learn on organic farms and smallholdings with people who are looking for volunteer help. WWOOF hosts offer food, accommodation and opportunities to learn about organic lifestyles. Volunteers give hands on help in return."

6. With regards to GM crops a noteworthy report titled *GMO Myths and Truths* is available on http://earthopensource.org/. This report arises from the work of scientists active in the field of genetics who seek for more transparent representation of scientific evidence that raises concerns about the production and consumption of GM organisms. See also Craig Holdrege *Genetics and the Manipulation of Life: The Forgotten Factor of Context.* (Hudson, NY: Indiscipline Press, 1996) and other resources available from The Nature Institute.

With regards to biodynamics—critical perspectives are presented by a number of authors, available through the internet. A website developed by Mark Moodie, *Considera—Developing Agriculture* (www.considera.org) has been created to compile and make available research in biodynamics from a wide range of perspectives. See also resources available on the Biodynamic Association website (www.biodynamics.com).

of these), and more towards grappling with what I see as the core issue lying at the root of both approaches—modified pigs or winterized oak bark: the issue of *consciousness*. Agriculture and culture are, from this standpoint, both expressions of *modes of consciousness*, and shedding light on these is the central thread being explored in the following pages.

This book arises from an engagement with core aspects of the biodynamic approach to land stewardship in order to attempt a deeper understanding for how our work with the land, with plants and animals, may be a catalyst not only for the transformation of compost and soil, but also for a *transformation* of consciousness. With this aim in mind I have set out to understand the kind of thinking that has given rise to the Enviropig, on the one hand, and the biodynamic preparations, on the other, in order to make visible the implications not only of these 'solutions' in applied form, but the implications for our own development which, I propose, they imply.

A healthy culture implies a healthy agriculture.

A Meteorological Journal

A few words on style.

The book that follows is not a manual on biodynamics. Many such resources exist, and with more attention to the innumerable themes and topics that this approach to land stewardship entails than will be covered in these pages. This book is also not a study that arises out of the still-dominant scientific paradigm which perpetuates the perspective that fundamental knowledge about nature and the human being can only arise from the 'detached' position of an 'objective observer.' The premise underlying this book is rather that a study such as the one recorded here involves a deep engagement of the whole person—in thought, yes, but also in feeling and in first hand experience arising from one's own actions.

My offering is therefore a record or account of a quite personal foray into the realm of possibilities, and challenges, that the biodynamic approach entails. It is a collected record of encounters, and the considerations they seeded.

The raw materials which provide the grist for these encounters are *muck* and *mind*. These terms are chosen with great care and respect.

Muck is all too often used to denote something that is dirty, unclean, unworthy (be it the product of either the back end of an animal or a way of thinking that has strayed off the path).

Mind-work is too often cast into an ivory tower, deemed 'unpractical,' abstract, or aloof.

A rift can arise between the two.

I use these terms together as acknowledgement of the lofty place that manure has in the biodynamic approach,[7] and of the potential for what is too often cast down as 'muck and magic' by a modern mindset, to bring *meaningful purpose* to the stewardship of land. This potential for a meaningful meeting between 'muck' and 'mind' is predicated, I suggest, on the entwined activity of hand, head, and heart—a re-engagement with multiple ways of knowing arising from the wholeness of human experience.

Annie Dillard, author and explorer of "natural facts and human meanings," uses the phrase (after Thoreau) "a meteorological journal of the mind" to describe her book *Pilgrim at Tinker Creek,* wherein she charts her forays into the natural world and the inner journey of mind

---

7. And indeed in many cultures worldwide who use it for any number of purposes—fuel for fires, as building material. Manure—and particularly cow manure—is therefore not 'muck' in the sense of being dirty and of no use, but rather is a precious product of the life process of the cow, and the basis for enlivening soil when prepared properly through composting.

and heart that these encounters evoked. The book you hold in your hands could perhaps be seen as sitting alongside the likes of *Pilgrim*—not in virtuosity or skill of authorship, but in kind—a charting of one individual's journey into a realm that presented itself as intriguing, mysterious, and beguiling on first encounter and that has required a range of approaches in order to come closer to a sense of its meaning and significance.

As Dillard reveals in *Pilgrim*, a frank account of personal experience can often elicit recognition in others, a singular lens accessible to many hearts and minds for the common questions that are posed by the author.

The pursuit of questions regarding the intertwined relationship between culture and agriculture have occupied me for many years. In order to stay true to the *unfolding* of this journey as a process involving my whole self—head, hand, and heart—over a period of *time*, the text that follows is a tapestry whose warp arises from first-hand experience[8] and reflection, and whose weft arises from the insights gained from the many teachers and guides I have encountered along the way. It is hoped that this weaving can be a valuable lens for those interested in questions of the intertwined life of the soil and the soul.

One last consideration is essential to note at the outset, and that is that I am no expert—no specialist in soil science, botany, microbiology, ruminant anatomy. I am neither farmer nor grower by profession. I am rather an amateur gardener and learn the craft through the spade. I am a lover of 'wild' places and have spent a lifetime encountering nature both on and off the path. I earn my daily bread as a teacher and researcher, and the four decades that I have spent on the Earth have not been wholly engaged in any one discipline or specific area of focus. I am thus a generalist and am acutely aware of both the gifts and challenges that that stance presents. In this regard I would once again place this book on Biodynamics alongside the likes of *Pilgrim at Tinker Creek* and other works of it's kind, which I would locate in the domain of the *naturalist*.

---

8. Throughout the text these experiential accounts and reflections are placed in italics. They are sourced from journals, lab note books, and in-the-moment musings arising out of the encounters described.

The naturalist has an approach to phenomena that alternates between the wide-angle view which is open to impressions from the 'field' and the sharp focus on the detail and specificity of the individual organism or event observed within that field. The naturalist is also more present in their own right, in the intimacy of their own responses and meaning-making, than is allowed to the scientific specialist.

My use of the term *naturalist* is, as I hope will become clear, more akin to the *natural philosopher* or *natural theologian* of the age of science which preceded the current trend toward reductionism and a scientism which has clinically removed the scientist from engagement with the arts, theology, or any endeavors deemed to lie outside their domain. Whereas there is undoubtedly a place for specialism in the questions I raise, it has become a concern of mine, evident throughout the text that follows, that a type of specialism developed and endorsed in the sciences over the last centuries contributes a *type of thinking* that is not necessarily the best *or only* path towards solutions, particularly when we are concerned with the realms of life.

As so, to take up the thread once again....

∞

Encountering Biodynamics

I first came across biodynamic methods in the early years of the 1990s while traveling and working in New Zealand. This first meeting 'brushed off,' as it were, and neither its theoretical nor its practical approach grabbed me at the time, for I was deeply immersed in the study of organic gardening and Permaculture.

Throughout my late twenties, I worked on several organic and biodynamic farms during travels in Australia, New Zealand, and North America, although I still did not engage deeply in the theory or principles that underlay the methods I was introduced to. This time was rather more focussed upon gaining some experience of the practical tasks involved in various approaches to land stewardship.

I later came upon biodynamics, again while studying in California. This was—quite literally—a meeting of more significance, a catalyst toward taking up a much deeper engagement with this less well known approach to agriculture, and the principles upon which it was founded.

∞

Fair Oaks, California   June 1995

Being a child of Ontario, Canada I had never come across that very American event which has its origins in New England in the early years of the settling of America, and which continues in several places today—a Town Hall Meeting.

Described by Thomas Jefferson as the "wisest invention ever devised by the wit of man for the perfect exercise of self-government," this type of social gathering clearly came with some commendation for its potential to address difficult or complex issues relevant to a wide slice of the community.

Well, suffice it to say that when I got wind of a Town Hall Meeting happening as part of an America Festival organized by members of my local community I decided then and there to attend. All the more so because the issue on the table was that of food and food production, which has interested me deeply ever since I landed at the age of eighteen on an organic farm outside Petitcodiac, New Brunswick and spent some intensive months gaining first hand experience of the gardening life.

Invited to the platform was a representative from Monsanto, a geneticist from UC Davis, and a local Biodynamic gardener.

Being early June, temperatures in the Sacramento valley were already hitting the 'head-for-cover' mark. Stepping into the church hall for the meeting, I couldn't help thinking that temperatures inside the meeting were likely to spike at some point that day as well, and that we might just be in for some sticky weather.

∞

Worlds Apart

We gathered in a local church hall, a large audience due to the obvious topical nature of the event. Each of the three main speakers had an opportunity to present their perspective, which was then followed by a question time and discussion period.

The Monsanto representative started with a presentation of which the dominant and unforgettable tone was one which presented his Corporation as working on behalf of the consumer, with the interest of the consumer squarely in mind. It was a well-polished public relations talk and did more to raise questions of how huge corporations can truly have the local and personal perspective at heart than it did to give me the confidence in his Company that he so clearly wished to instill.

The geneticist was the second of the three to speak. Here we were presented with the picture that humankind has for thousands of years been 'improving' on plants and animals in order to enhance aspects of their growth and productivity through breeding and selection, and that in the contemporary genetic engineering paradigm there is essentially no difference. This argument was delivered accompanied by a presentation of Mendel's work and the identification of genetic dominance revealed through his efforts. Throughout this second of the three presentations there was an appeal made to a particular kind of logic which placed the genetic modification of plants in a linear pathway of development that reached from the initial selection and breeding of grains thousands of years ago to the emergent possibilities of designer organisms and foods which were being worked on in science labs around the world. When questioned, there was—for the geneticist—no need to be concerned when scientists began to manipulate the genetic material from organisms who would in no way interbreed or mix naturally, violating the species barriers in the process. For her, this did not mark a significant departure in the manner in which humans intervened in natural processes, but merely elaborated—with more technical sophistication (expertise even?)—age old practices.

The third speaker, a biodynamic gardener, gave a well-intentioned and heart-felt speech about locally produced food and the significance of *quality* over quantity that—though it spoke to a largely sympathetic audience—was clearly lacking the analytical thoroughness of the geneticist or the practiced phrasing of the Monsanto representative. The presentation was strong on the side of sentimentality but came across as lacking 'substance' and—following the geneticist—an attitude of scientific 'rigor.'[9]

A certain trichotomy of approaches emerged throughout the Town Hall meeting—the geneticist clearly appealing to our powers of logic and analytical thought with a healthy dose of an appeal to the authority of the scientific method, the Biodynamic gardener to our feeling life and sense of 'rightness,' and the Monsanto representative to a kind of social and economic 'good' which was—he strove to make clear—embodied in the modern corporation.

In the question period and discussion that followed the presentations, the dialog (which did indeed become rather heated) changed from being an initially convivial sharing of perspectives to an entrenched withdrawal behind various arguments and platitudes. All three speakers found themselves on an increasingly polarized platform.

I was left feeling that this was a clear example of the seemingly impossible task of bridging professions, or paradigms, and that the speakers were 'worlds apart,'[10] their perspectives irreconcilable.

I was struck, and quite affronted, by a statement by the geneticist to the effect that unless we (the audience) were trained genetic scientists we did not—in the end—really have a voice or opinion in the question of the appropriateness or otherwise of genetically modifying organisms and we should 'trust' the expertise of the scientists who 'knew' what they were doing. As we were discussing the manipulation of foodstuffs intended for public consumption this comment felt, to me, like a slap in the face and came across as a certain arrogance and elitism in the unquestioning authority of science.

I was left with a host of questions that have simmered in my mind for many years:

- Do the scientific specialists know what they are doing?
  How do they know what they are doing?

---

9. I do not intend to criticize any of the individuals described in this section, merely to describe the experience—as a listener—of the various perspectives presented.

10. This is a tangential reference to the book *Worlds Apart* by Owen Barfield which takes 8 people and their seemingly 'watertight compartments' of professional interest and through a fictional dialogue illustrates the challenges presented by intellectual specialization for a 'true meeting' of minds.

- What is the relationship between science and agriculture? Is agriculture a science?

- Is the ever more prevalent (and seemingly un-questioned) marriage between science and agriculture well founded?

With regards to the way in which Biodynamics in particular was represented in the Town Hall meeting, I was left with the questions:

- Can biodynamics 'come to the table?'

- Can biodynamics be understood by the same scientific consciousness that has developed out of a study the inanimate world?

- What way of knowing would be 'adequate' to gain an understanding of the practices employed by the biodynamic gardener?

The example given of the Oak Bark preparation (and the preparations generally) raise still further questions:

- Is biodynamics a science? A ritual? An instance of the proverbial 'Muck and Magic?'

Big questions, and not easily addressed.

∞

The Enviropig and the Oak Bark preparation come into the agricultural domain through—it would appear—synthetic thinking processes that are attempting to create beneficial solutions to specific farming issues. Out of 'parts'—genetic information from mice, *e. coli* bacteria, skulls, oak bark—a new synthesis or 'whole' is created. In the case of the Enviropig a thought process is evident and explicit that, through its mechanistic or 'cause and effect' elements, reveals a type of logic familiar for its dominant role in much of our current thinking. It runs something like this (in a much abbreviated version): pigs don't digest phosphates in their feed well—pig effluent is high in phosphates—these become an environmental pollutant—through genetic engineering pigs can be genetically altered to produce phytase in their saliva—through this intervention a more complete digestion of the phosphates can be achieved—lower levels of phosphates pass into their effluent—lower environmental pollutant risk.[11]

In terms of the Oak Bark preparation it is not so easy to grasp the synthesis of plant and animal substances, their process of preparation or, in fact, their application protocol. The familiar logic that seems to lie behind the choice of 'parts' and their combination that the creators of the Enviropig have chosen seems to be missing in the instance of the Oak Bark preparation. A causal connection between the skull of a domestic animal, oak bark, and a specified period of time for internment in the ground is not initially apparent. Furthermore, how the substance that results from this 'preparation' can be effective in the relatively minute proportions[12] in which it is applied beggars belief. What is being proposed here?

The experience of the Town Hall meeting on the one hand, and the conundrum presented by the nature of the 'parts' which comprised the Oak Bark preparation on the other, spurred me on to seek for ways of understanding the innovations proposed by Rudolf Steiner in his suggestions for a renewal of agriculture. As a child of the twentieth century, schooled in materialism, reductionism, positivism, and very conscious that my way of seeing the world is still largely informed by these, I needed to see if I could find a way of 'standing inside' the biodynamic perspective. I came to the conclusion, having spent some time considering both of the examples above, that biodynamics presents methods and practices (such as the creation and use of the field and compost preparations) which are very different from those which derive from analytical, mechanistic modes of thought and that by their very nature, these methods and practices present the challenge of *understanding* to the practitioner.

---

11. More detail about the Enviropig and the background for its breeding can be found at www.uoguelph.ca/enviropig/

12. For an average sized compost heap, a pea-sized ball of preparation incorporated in a small handful of humus and inserted in the compost pile.

I decided to set out to find for myself a way toward a deeper understanding of what was going on with the biodynamic preparations, or else I would have to admit that they were indeed the product of a way of thinking that is inaccessible or incomprehensible and thus the preparations themselves would have to be used by faith alone—or forgotten.

The question is (and was for me) where to start?

2

Digging In

"It goes among things that change..."

Biodynamics: Origins

Concerns regarding the waning fertility and vitality in crop and herd inspired agriculturalists to approach Rudolf Steiner in the early twentieth century with a request for some advice as to how to address these new challenges.

Rudolf Steiner's response was to give a series of eight lectures, now known as the Agriculture Course. These lectures mark the seed-point of this new initiative which has today spread throughout the world. Taken purely on their own terms, the record we have of these lectures leaves an awful lot in the readers' hands in terms of puzzling out the ideas and practical approaches proposed there. When the biodynamic preparations are described in lectures 4 and 5, indications are given for bringing plant substances (bark, flowers, leafy stems) together with animal organs (bladders, intestines), along with indications for how these combined substances should be treated. Most are buried in the ground, some over the winter months, some over the summer months. Whereas brief indications are given for what the resulting preparation will serve once inserted into a compost pile,[13] for the practitioner wishing to build a conscious bridge between the preparation materials (plant and animal) and the processes for which they were designed to support, a great deal of further research and understanding is needed. Otherwise the preparations are merely recipes to be followed and applied, but without an understanding of the principles that lie behind the particular choice of materials proposed by Steiner in their creation. Perhaps more significantly, without a grasp of these principles, the practitioner will lack the insight for the design of new preparations to meet conditions not experienced a century ago, of which there are any number today.

---

13. The addition of the preparations is indicated as stabilizing nitrogen, 'enlivening the soil,' making the 'manure inwardly more sensitive and receptive,' making the soil 'more intelligent.'

Attendees of these initial lectures given in Koberwitz became the first biodynamic practitioners, and also the first researchers and teachers of these new methods. Now, after almost 90 years of practice and research into biodynamics, there is a sizeable body of literature covering a wide range of aspects of both principles and methods.[14]

As a teacher myself, and someone who regularly contributes to biodynamic education, the preparations present a particularly interesting challenge when it comes to introducing this still novel approach to a new group of students, or even to apprentices who have become adept at making preparations, but are still grappling with trying to understand the principles that stand behind these otherwise mystical creations in a more conscious way.

The question often arises: has science not moved on from mucking about with animal organs and seasonal burial practices?

∞

Learning the Trade

Spring, 2013

It is getting on now into a new year of growth and greenery, and spring has most definitely sprung.

There is now some warmth in the sun as it shines on my latest enterprise, which I am undertaking on a table on the back patio behind our house.

I am stuffing a stag's bladder with yarrow flowers…yes, a stag's bladder. With yarrow flowers.

Once stuffed I am going to find a good sunny spot so that I can hang it up throughout the coming summer and then, when the next season of mellow fruitfulness rolls around, it will go into the ground for the winter.

The well-stuffed bladder comes out looking not at all unlike a floral haggis, an admittedly odd thing to hang in the sunlight for the coming months. But hey ho, it's worth a go!

---

14. The Biodynamic Association (BDA) has published a list of literature on their website, http://www.biodynamic.org.uk/shop/full-booklist.html, which is one source for an overview of existing literature.

This particular act of 'preparation' making began on an afternoon in early autumn last year, when my wife, our two girls and I went down to the canal near Frampton-on-Severn for one of our favorite weekend walks.

We often head out of the valleys in which we live on a Sunday afternoon into the open land adjacent to the Severn estuary for some big sky and to check out the canal boats. We like to indulge ourselves in a bit of wistfulness, imagining that canal-side, narrowboat life would present a simplification to the busy lives of work and school that fill the week. It is also a great destination to aim for in order to indulge in that most English of rituals—tea time—and throughout the warmer months a great cream tea can be had in a Wonderland garden off the canal path, through a hole in the hedge, with a beech-tree swing for girls...

Last autumn, while we were out on one of our walks, we found our attention drawn away from the boats lining the canal and found ourselves enticed, instead, to the hedgerows and verges that flank the canal path.

Sloes were ready for picking, and elder berries drooped darkly in thick bunches just within arms reach. Clusters of blackberries framed the fruity-autumnal scene, poised amongst the far-reaching stalks of thorny boughs.

While the others set to wild-harvesting this rich abundance, I wandered off down the canal path to investigate its leafy banks.

I was soon struck by the sight of tall white flowers that everywhere reached out upright and strong along the grassy banks on either side of the path and, on closer inspection, recognized the unmistakable feathery leaf and tightly clustered umbel of a familiar flower...

I first met this plant when a fascination with the I Ching gripped me many years ago. I next came across it when making compost while WWOOFing in New Zealand. A small nut-sized portion of some dark looking substance had been mixed with humus and stuffed into a big pile of carefully layered compost. Intriguing, peculiar...taken on as part of an overall openness to encounters with the unfamiliar. Yarrow tea or tincture had found its way into the house at one time or another to join other medicines in the family medicine cupboard.

But on that autumnal walk along the banks of the canal, I met yarrow in a different way, with a different set of considerations than divination or medication. This meeting sparked in me the stirrings of a new mission—to collect the bright white umbels and to find myself a stag's bladder.

By the day's end I had a large bag stuffed full of white flower heads.

Throughout the winter the yarrow hung in cloth bags from the rafters of my workshop and now, six months after that canal-side jaunt, I have retrieved the yarrow from its winter storage and found—to my delight—that friend Ed had a stag's bladder to spare (!)

And so, with all the necessaries to hand—and a sunny spring morning to spend—I remove the dried flower heads from their stalks, dampen them with a tea made from yarrow blossoms and begin to stuff the bladder.

Before long I have a nicely packed—if slightly odd—floral package ready to spend a summer in the sunlight.

Now, where shall I hang it?....

Faced with the conundrums presented by the Oak Bark preparation I was inspired to dig a bit deeper. Taking this quite literally, I began to make the preparations proposed by Rudolf Steiner in his Agriculture course.

Obtaining the different plant and animal components of the preparations is a stimulating process in itself. It is quite exhilarating to encounter a plant in its native habitat, to pick and harvest the plant, and to set it to dry ready for prep-making. When done as part of a process aimed at enhancing soil vitality and the quality of life, there is a sense of meaningful purpose that accompanies the harvest, even when one is at the same time stepping into the unknown of a new undertaking.

To hold in one's hand a cow horn, a crystal that is bound for crushing, or the sublime geometry of yarrow is to hold something both manifestly physical and stolidly material on the one hand, and—on the other—objects of deep mystery and wonder.

Whereas I found (and still find) the making of the preparations to be a central part of learning about biodynamics and its methods, there lingers for me, within the practical tasks of prep-making, echoes of the Town Hall meeting and the questions that arose at that time. These revolve around the meaning of what the biodynamic practitioner is engaged with in the making of preparations. Why a skull? … and why the bark of a tree? … and why the particular choice of plant, and animal organs?

How can all these parts of plants and deceased animals contribute anything to the 'down-to-earth' tasks of producing food?

The *why* and *wherefore* of the particular components of each preparation described by Steiner (and for that matter, the why and wherefore of preparations created since, or yet to be created) became a central pursuit for me. This path pointed to questions not just of practicalities but to the very core of our attitudes toward nature and, for that 'matter,' … of mind.

Paradigm of Biodynamics

A significant contribution to this quest for deeper understanding arose for me through an encounter with the work of Dr. Andrew Lorand—a farmer, gardener, teacher, and researcher in Biodynamics. Dr. Lorand's PhD dissertation presents a paradigmatic analysis of the Biodynamic method. He describes a catalyst to his own research in the introduction to a condensed version of his dissertation:

> When the author mentioned biodynamic agriculture in
> conversations with extension agents and teachers of agriculture
> around the United States, most had not heard of it. With the
> passage of the 1990 Farm Bill, which includes the regulation
> and certification of organic produce, however, more agents and
> teachers can expect questions about this worldwide movement.
> Primary sources on biodynamic agriculture are not easy to find.
> Furthermore, these books use language and describe concepts that
> are outside most agricultural educators' frames of reference. The
> problem is to describe biodynamic agriculture in terms that are
> accessible to extension agents and teachers of agriculture. (p.1)

Lorand tackles the task of making the principles of biodynamic agriculture "more accessible" through a comparison of biodynamics with "traditional agriculture," "conventional agriculture" and "organic agriculture." In taking this approach, Lorand recognizes that biodynamics arises out of a very different paradigm than what has informed much of our contemporary science and conventional approaches to agriculture. Lorand's thesis steps off from the work of Egon Guba who writes:

> paradigms (the set of beliefs that guide action, whether they
> are everyday actions or actions taken in connection with a
> disciplined inquiry) can be best analyzed by answering three
> specific questions: (a) what is the nature of reality (ontology),
> (b) what is the nature of the relationship between the knower
> and that reality (epistemology), and (c) how should the knower
> (the practitioner) use that knowledge concerning that reality in
> practice (methodology)? (Lorand, p.2)

This excursion into the work of Dr. Lorand pointed towards two things. On the one hand, it helped make comprehensible the experience I had during the Town Hall meeting that the speakers had not 'met.' They had presented their perspectives, and these perspectives contrasted with each other so poignantly because what was not explicit was that each perspective arose from a different paradigm, a way of seeing which was not made visible. This crucial aspect of the different speakers' points of view remained hidden.

The second outcome of my encounter with Lorand's work was a reminder that, along with the practical engagement with the burying of ground crystals in horns and the stuffing of bladders with the flowers of *Achillea millefolium,* I would do well—in seeking to understand the biodynamic preparations—to pick up one of these core elements of the *paradigmatic analysis* undertaken by Lorand—that of epistemology—and to see what light a study of epistemology could shed on the new approaches to farming and gardening proposed by Steiner.

The Art of Knowing

Epistemology, also known as 'theory of knowledge,' is generally regarded as a branch of philosophy concerned with understanding the act of knowing. By posing questions such as 'how do we know what we know?,' 'how is knowledge acquired?' and 'what is knowledge?' an epistemological enquiry directs attention to the very activity that lies at the root of all sciences, arts and—in fact—to the foundation of our everyday cognitive activity. Addressing as it does the very nature of how we know the world, and ourselves, the question could be asked when considering the field of epistemology whether we are dealing with merely a *branch* of the discipline of philosophy (and something best left to philosophers) or something of much more far-reaching importance. I have come, through my own delving into this realm, to throw in my lot with the latter.

The context for epistemological enquiry

In my own experience of formal education, epistemology as a subject of study had little to no attention, its formal engagement only arising in my mid-twenties. It was in fact generally the case that all of the subjects—mathematics, history, science, language, arts—which were taught to me as a school boy in Southern Ontario, were taught in such a way as to seem 'free' of epistemological considerations. This omission was clearly essential in the early years of my formal education—as an engagement with epistemology requires a certain maturity of cognitive development and self-reflective capacity.

It is quite remarkable, however, that once we emerge as self-reflective learners, epistemology as a subject of study is still not generally engaged with alongside the actual subject matter of the sciences, medical disciplines, politics, and economics—which are powerful shaping influences in all of our lives.

Albert Einstein, a physicist known both in and outside the scientific domain, writes:

> The eyes of the scientist are directed upon those phenomena which are accessible to observation, upon their apperception and conceptual formulation. In the attempt to achieve a conceptual formulation of the confusingly immense body of observational data, the scientist makes use of a whole arsenal of concepts of which he imbibed practically with his mother's milk; and seldom if ever is he aware of the eternally problematic character of his concepts. He uses this conceptual material, or, speaking more exactly, these conceptual tools of thought, as something obviously, immutably given; something having an objective value of truth which is hardly ever, and in any case not seriously, to be doubted. How could this be otherwise? How would the ascent of a mountain be possible, if the use of hands, legs and tools had to be sanctioned step by step on the basis of the science of mechanics? And yet in the interests of science it is necessary over and over again to engage in the critique of these fundamental concepts, in order that we may not unconsciously be ruled by them. This becomes evident especially in those situations involving development of ideas in which the consistent use of the traditional fundamental concepts leads us to paradoxes difficult to resolve.[15]

---

15. From the foreword written by Einstein to Max Jammer's book, *Concepts of Space; The History of Theories of Space in Physics.*

From a different, but related perspective, the educator Parker Palmer makes the following statement: "Every way of knowing becomes a way of living, every epistemology becomes an ethic."[16] These two perspectives on the significance of turning our attention to examine fundamental aspects of our cognitive activity, drawn from a scientist in the first instance and an educator in the second, can be applied more widely to other significant aspects of cultural life.

Take for instance the fact that we have, on any given day, access to any number of accounts of events in both the human and natural worlds which pose serious threats to the integrity of social and ecological systems.[17] In many of these examples, concerted effort is expended to ameliorate, mitigate, or diffuse these potential threats—the creation of modified pigs or biodynamic preparations, for instance. However, in seeking the source of the evident dissonances experienced in our everyday lives and activities, we could ask—how often is an investigation of our "conventional epistemology" undertaken? How often do we investigate and re-evaluate the very epistemological roots that inform our individual and cultural actions?

In contemporary western cultural life, the disciplined engagement with philosophy and epistemology has largely become holed up in university departments, often as specialized branches of the humanities undertaken by professional academics. Only very rarely do we find mention of the "cutting edge" discoveries in the realms of epistemology outside of these specialized domains. When, for instance, do we hear politicians making reference to important philosophical points of view that are being considered in the shaping of policy—of peoples lives? It is instead the authority of science that is often called upon in contemporary political discourse or decision making, no longer the authority of the church and certainly not the authority arising from self or collective epistemological reflection.

---

16. Quoted by Zajonc (2006, p. 3)

17. It is not my intention to go into these in detail, we need only consider the many themes that "headline" in our current culture of reporting—pollution, political turmoil, climate change, peak oil and its implications, genetic modification of living beings, hunger...

When weight of opinion is given to science, as it was by the geneticist in the Town Hall meeting, scientific disciplines are themselves rooted in epistemological frameworks (to which Einstein draws our attention in the passage above) that are very rarely made explicit and are often unexamined. This is also true of the publication of scientific discoveries or new technological innovations. Very rarely is the epistemological root—the *way of seeing and knowing*—made explicit. It is rather too often the case that scientific knowledge is presented as having arisen from a place of complete neutrality, objectivity, and impartiality. It is presented as being 'value free'—'the view from nowhere.' This has radical implications, and raises a third key element in Palmer's statement, that ways of knowing are *fundamentally* ethical—even when they claim to be "objective" in the sense that this is sometimes meant, i.e. of being free of moral or ethical considerations.

The implication that lies at the heart of Palmer's statement is that, far from epistemology being an activity that is best left to academic specialities or even, and this perhaps is more challenging, far from being optional, epistemology is everybody's business and this because it is *essentially* ethical.

Every way of knowing becomes a way of living.

If there is truth in Palmer's statement, epistemology and the epistemological foundation for our way of living—both public and private—requires a much deeper engagement and examination than it is commonly given.

In what follows I will describe three perspectives from contemporary thinkers which have greatly informed my own forays into this field. These are of course merely a selection of the many contributions to the study of epistemology that could be explored, and they represent a selection made by me in the course of my own exploration into the realm of biodynamics. This said, although they by no means represent the wide field of study from which they are drawn, they are, nonetheless, highly significant in what they reveal in terms of ways of knowing for the disciplines of science, of consciousness studies and for new innovative methods for the preparation of compost.

Ways of knowing: three perspectives

The demotion of direct experience: Ronald Brady

I will begin this exploration of *ways of knowing* with a look at the work of philosopher Ronald Brady, in particular through his contributions to the book *Being on Earth* (2006). Brady describes his journey as being one that began in the study of chemistry but that led eventually to the study of philosophy due to the encounters he had early on with the *way in which* science was pursued. In "Memories of a Wrong Minded Student," he recalls:

> When I began college as a chemistry major, my enthusiasm for science was somewhat dampened by meeting a professor of chemistry who pointed out the difference between my own goals and those he, as an experienced professional, would call mature. My passion, he noted, was entirely focused on direct experience. My sense of chemical change was invested in sensible qualities: in smells, colors, the effervescence of liquids, the appearance of precipitates, the light and violence of flame, and so on. But, he countered, this was probably closer to medieval alchemy than to chemistry. Chemistry is really a matter of molecular and atomic events of which we can have only a theoretical grasp. By contrast, the sensible experience on which my excitement centered was secondary—it was not the external reality but merely the effect of that on the human senses.

Brady encountered what still lives in much popular teaching and reporting of science, as well as in education generally, throughout much of our western culture. This is a deep-seated distrust of our un-mediated sense life as a door to knowledge about "the world." Brady writes in the chapter titled "Direct Experience":

> One of the difficulties with scientific accounts of the world is their apparent insistence on an "objective" reality that cannot be directly experienced, with the resulting demotion of experience—what our senses make out of the world—to a mere show that differs substantially from "what is really there." This is something we all know and do not think about very much. (2006, p. 12)

Having had several more encounters with professors who made it very clear to Brady that his interest in science as an *experiential* approach to knowledge was misguided and 'unprofessional,' he felt a waning of enthusiasm for the study of chemistry. "My first reaction was to feel the world of chemistry, which had previously contained some of the most beautiful and mysterious experiences of the natural world, now becoming gray, dry, and lifeless. My second reaction was to leave chemistry."

Brady's path led him into the literature department, where he pursued his exploration of the role of *experience* in understanding the world and where he proposed a dissertation on the crossover between scientific observation and aesthetic experience in Goethe's science. Again he met resistance and a lack of acceptance for his proposal. "Aesthetic experience, they repeated knowingly, is important to literature but not to science."

In the philosophy department Brady found a setting where he could pursue his studies and these become the basis for his contribution to *Being on Earth*. Brady sets out to unravel the developments in scientific thinking that led to the types of encounters he experienced first-hand with a science that had become abstract and largely theoretical in its approach to natural phenomena. He makes evident a particularly poignant contribution to this "one-eyed color blind onlooker"[18] approach to science and its view of the role of the senses in cognitive life in the work of Galileo.[19]

Galileo's significant act of distinguishing primary and secondary qualities in observed phenomena is often referred to as an essential contribution to the development of modern science, of the modern scientific method. Brady refers to this moment as a central event in the *demotion* of

---

18. See Lehrs (1985) for a further elaboration of this term. It refers to the resulting mindset that the scientist adopts if rigidly following the tenets of a science based on the removal of the subject (the subjective) in the attempt to obtain objective, universally applicable knowledge of the world.

19. Galileo's thinking, and its subsequent influence on modern science is complex. E. A. Burt gives a thorough description of Galileo's view that "nature is the domain of mathematics" (Burt, 2003)—an essentially epistemological statement. Galileo, in this light, is one of several influential thinkers whose science derives from a philosophical stance we could call mathematism.

direct experience in the pursuit of scientific knowledge. It is a demotion with much wider implications for the discipline of science, however, for from that time on the human being "begins to appear for the first time in the history of thought as an irrelevant spectator and insignificant effect of the great mathematical system which is the substance of reality" (Burt, 2003, p. 90). It is this relegation of the subject and his or her unmediated sense experience to a secondary (and either insignificant or potentially inappropriate) role in the acquisition of knowledge and truth that Brady wrestles with in *Being on Earth*.

Now, to most of us, the experience of being a subject separate from a world of objects—many of which seem to not present their essential being to our senses—seems self-evident. It is, as it were, the nature of reality we emerge or mature into, as a *given*. This naïve-realistic stance (as it is referred to philosophically) toward the perceived world lies at the basis of much of modern cultural experience. It is the experience that I have of being a distinct subject who perceives a world of objects separate from myself and external to each other. Furthermore, this world seems self-evidently to exist—to be *there*—without my contributing to its manifestation in any way. On the contrary, I experience it as manifest and myself as a (on the whole) passive recipient of impressions arising from my encounter with *it*.

There is, however, more to this experience than meets the eye.

Cognitive amnesia: Henri Bortoft

> *"The 'self-entity' itself emerges from the process of cognition and is not there as such beforehand."*

The problems—of knowledge, of philosophy, of science, of living—that arise from the subject/object divide which both our everyday cognition and our disciplined scientific research are based upon have been explored at length by a wide range of authors. They have occupied the human mind from the time when the medieval view of Man as Microcosm of the great Macrocosm began to wane (more on this subject to follow). An earlier unified worldview essentially gave way to the later—and still dominant—dualistic worldview.

Though it does a disservice to this vast chapter of human thought not to go deeper into the various authors who have engaged the significant issues raised regarding the nature of knowing, of consciousness, and of conscience, it would expand this study beyond reasonable bounds. It is maybe enough to say that since the time of Galileo[20] we have struggled with the problem of whether it is our *thinking* or our *sense activity* that can be relied upon to give us "true" knowledge of either our self or the world in which we find ourselves.

Coupled with this is the deep-seated problem of *subjective* versus *objective* knowledge, articulated by Brady so clearly in his contributions to *Being on Earth*. In the twentieth century, work undertaken in the history and philosophy of science contributed new light to these thorny issues. Henry Bortoft is one author who has made significant contributions to the problems of knowledge.

Setting out to look, from a philosophical point of view, at the way in which J. W. Goethe approached his studies in natural science, Bortoft has shed light on significant aspects of our cognitive life.

Using an ambiguous figure of what appears to be a "random patchwork of black and white areas" in a circular frame, Bortoft presents a very striking experience of the relationship between our *sensory* activity and our *thinking* activity.

After a time, and with our intentional activity directed toward the image, a figure emerges from the previously chaotic ground of black and

---

20. I think it important to reference Galileo in this manner; instead of saying "since Galileo" I have chosen "since the time of Galileo" to indicate the possibility that Galileo was *one* exponent of a shift in consciousness that was, on all levels—physiologically, psychologically, and spiritually—giving the human subject a greater awareness of themselves as separate cognizing beings, centered within their own individual point of view. This idea references the research of Rudolf Steiner and the substantial evidence for the evolution of consciousness articulated in his own work as well as in the work of Ernst Lehrs, Owen Barfield, and others. The choice of wording is such as to indicate that the shift in consciousness is a supra-personal event. Galileo, however, is one of the earliest and clearest proponents of modes of thinking arising from this new experience of self and world—with profound implications. Burt writes: "The form of the primary-secondary doctrine in Galileo is worth a moment's pause, for its effects in modern thought have been of incalculable importance. It is a fundamental step toward that banishing of man from the great world of nature and his treatment as an effect of what happens in the latter..." (2003, p. 89).

white patches. A giraffe's head is "seen." There is much to be gleaned from this experience, as in time the initial effort expended to attempt to see some organization within the seeming chaos of black and white shapes, which gives rise to "seeing the giraffe"—eventually reverses so that a considerable attentional effort is required to not-see the giraffe.

This *experience* becomes a bridge to the realization that whereas much—in fact the majority—of our everyday cognitive life is rooted in the assumption that we encounter the world and its objects as if they were just "there" (naïve empiricism), in actual fact what we are no longer aware of is the organizing activity through which these objects become apparent. The difficulty is that we are no longer aware of that side of the cognitive act which contributes to the "seeing," as this is no longer reliant on an activity of will.

Bortoft refers to this conundrum as "cognitive amnesia" (1996, p. 139)—amnesia because in our cognitive perception as we naively experience it, we no longer are conscious of the fact that we only see or experience anything due to the *organizing idea* that imbues with meaning the otherwise chaotic life of pure sense perception. I quote Bortoft at length in what follows due to the clarity of his explanation, and the significance that this has for cognitive activity:

All scientific knowledge, then, is a correlation of *what* is seen with the *way* it is seen. When the "way of seeing" is invisible [...] then we live on the empirical level where it seems to be self-evident that

discoveries are made directly through the senses. In this "natural attitude" we have no sense of our own participation, and hence we seem
to ourselves to be onlookers to a world which is fixed and finished.
Forgetfulness of the way of seeing is the origin of empiricism, which
is still by far the most popular philosophy of science, in spite of all the
discoveries in the history and philosophy of science, which show that
it is a philosophy of cognitive amnesia. (*Ibid.*, pp. 138-9)

The realization of the nature of cognition revealed in the above, and
developed much further by Bortoft in his book, has massive implications
for consciousness—be it scientifically engaged or otherwise. Bortoft's
articulation of the role of the *organizing idea* in cognitive perception—
only briefly touched upon above—allows him to come to the striking
realization that "we live within a dimension of mind which is as invisible
to us as the air we breathe" (*Ibid.*, p. 141).[21]

Insight into the role of the organizing idea in cognitive perception
is particularly relevant to my experience of the Town Hall meeting for,
with this realization in mind, it is possible to understand that the geneticist from UC Davis and our local biodynamic gardener were undertaking their studies of natural phenomena with quite radically different
organizing ideas. This leads to the very important fact that 'pig' for the one

---

21. The role of what Bortoft refers to as the organizing idea in cognitive perception has also
been revealed through the work of Von Senden, Oliver Sacks, and others. These studies,
which focussed on the experience of individuals who were blinded from birth but whose
sight was eventually restored through medical science are relevant to mention. Annie Dillard
makes reference to Von Senden's research *Space and Sight* when she writes that for the newly
sighted vision is "pure sensation unencumbered by meaning" (Dillard, 1974).

is not at all the same 'pig' as it is for the other. The fact that this was not recognized or stated as a contributing factor to the different perspectives meant that no fruitful meeting or dialog could take place.

Understanding the role of the *organizing idea in cognitive perception* could profoundly influence the way in which we do science, the way we educate in the broadest sense, and indeed to the way in which we engage in everyday life. It could allow us to grasp the idea that in order to address the issues we encounter in the realm of agriculture (and in culture more widely) that threaten health and wellbeing, we would be wise to undertake a concerted investigation into an otherwise invisible "dimension of mind."

A collective disease: Georg Kühlewind

Where Brady highlights the origins of the "split"[22] and Henri Bortoft follows at great length and with true virtuosity the epistemological intricacies of the contemporary mind, Georg Kühlewind is, I feel, an essential thinker to mention in the present context due to the way in which he has examined and described an all too often overlooked aspect in our life of consciousness. He does so through a study of both the biographical and historical development of consciousness as revealed through such diverse phenomena as the development of language and speech, the phenomenology of the processes of thinking and perceiving, and the nature of art.

Kühlewind's conclusion, reminiscent of Bortoft's *cognitive amnesia*, is that modern consciousness is diseased.

This quite striking pronouncement appears and is elaborated at some length in his book *From Normal to Healthy* (1988).

Kühlewind describes the diseased consciousness as being a collective disease—and as such it generally goes unrecognized. Having a certain

---

22. The term "split" is used here to refer to the separation of perception into primary and secondary qualities, the separation of thinking and perceiving and the development of the subject/object consciousness. "The world is […] a non-dual world that we split—or is split by our "ego" or "me" consciousness—into subject-object, self-other, friend-enemy, humanity-nature and so on" (Kühlewind, 2008, p.11).

resonance with Bortoft's articulation of everyday cognition, i.e. a cognition that no longer experiences the role of thinking in the objects we perceive and therefore mistakes the perceived object as a *given*, Kühlewind attributes the causes of the disease to mistaken experience or mis-identification. His argument is rooted in both historical (cultural) and individual (developmental) observations that differentiate between two levels of consciousness.

The *superconscious*, Kühlewind proposes, is the realm from which all other elements of consciousness arise.

The superconscious is the realm of the living activity of the "I" of the human. As the living, dynamic source and seat of consciousness the superconscious is not generally witnessed or included in our account of our experience because of its primacy and the fact that it is the very wellspring of consciousness itself.

In trying to illuminate the elusive and difficult task of bringing this aspect of consciousness to experience one encounters such sayings as "you're looking for the ox you're riding on" (Kühlewind, 1988, p. 53). In Zen Buddhism *koans* were used to engage the mind in such a way that that which is not normally experienced was revealed through a type of *metanoia* brought about by the intense contemplation of an illogical story or question. Kühlewind offers something of a *koan* for our modern mind with the phrase "the past *is,* the present *becomes,*" a phrase which seeks to point consciousness toward its source as well as highlighting the challenge of experiencing the superconscious *becoming* of our everyday awareness. The question arises from the above; how then can we say that the superconscious exists if it cannot be experienced directly?

Let us look at how the superconscious may *indirectly* be revealed. Kühlewind points toward such a possibility with the question: "how can a being who neither speaks nor thinks learn words, language and thinking?" This is for linguistic science quite a conundrum to this day. The first words that a child speaks must be learned without words or explanations!

> Children understand their first words directly, without words, intuitively. Or, to put it another way, they understand through

such a deep internal imitation of the speaker that they "imitate"
not only the words but the meaning of the intended speech.
They identify themselves with the source of speaking,
which is the "I" of the speaker. They have no other way of
understanding anything: no explanations are possible.
(*Ibid.*, p. 25)

Through the above exploration, much abbreviated it must be said,
Kühlewind goes on to conclude that:

By observing the child's acquisition of speech and thought, we
can see that this process requires the faculties of thinking, feeling
and willing in order for the child to develop into a speaking adult.
Yet these faculties function quite differently in the child and adult.
We might say that they are not yet separated from one another
for the child, but form a single faculty [...] it might be called a
superconscious ability. (*Ibid.*, p.28)

From this example of early speech acquisition Kühlewind goes on
to follow the development of consciousness whereby these initially superconscious faculties and capacities give rise to formations and habits
of thinking, feeling, and willing which are no longer form-free but very
much individualized and often quite fixed or formed (Bortoft's ambiguous image of the giraffe was designed to illustrate this process.) This
realm of soul is designated by Kühlewind as the *subconscious*.

Everyday consciousness, for the adult at least, is positioned between
the two realms of consciousness and—as in the example of cognitive
perception given above—everyday experience is generally oriented toward the finished forms of thought and feeling and does not experience that activity by which these contents of experience arise. It is the
superconscious from which the everyday contents of consciousness are
surveyed and witnessed but as consciousness is conscious of these contents and not of its present awareness, the former has the characteristic
of being much more "real." Kühlewind's far-reaching study can be encapsulated in the sentence "Our consciousness is a past consciousness,
conscious of its own past" (*Ibid.*, p. 15).

Summary

Having set out to explore the potential far-reaching implications of epistemology in the context of a study of biodynamics, and having offered three contributions toward an understanding of contemporary ways of knowing, we find the following situation. In the realm of science (as for our everyday cognition), the "objects" of our awareness are experienced as "given" (be they pigs, trees, crystals, plants, or cow horns). The process of consciousness that "objectifies" them in the first place is not experienced (Bortoft's *cognitive amnesia*) and therefore the *way of knowing* which is implicit in the way in which they are seen is not made evident. This gives rise to a philosophical stance that is called 'positivism,' a position that is still implicit in much contemporary scientific work.

The self or subject lacks true self-experience due to the "disease of consciousness" (Kühlewind) and comes to doubt or even deny its own existence,[23] an event that is made evident in the field of science in the supposed removal of the scientist from the activity of science under the auspices of objectivity and the search for pure knowledge—the 'view from nowhere.' This creates a false sense that 'truth' or 'facts' exist in their own right, irrespective of the individual whose cognitive activity *organizes them* in particular ways.

Because the superconscious realm out of which both *self* and *object* arise (or become 'posited') is no longer experienced, 'reality' becomes ever more displaced into an abstract, quality-less realm accessible only to the dis-embodied mind (Brady). This state of affairs gives rise to a materialist and mechanistic *way of knowing* and results in a science ('search for knowledge') which has removed itself from an engagement with the

---

23. We refer to the Human *being*, and in earlier times Nature itself was perceived to be populated by *beings*, whose works were the phenomena of nature perceived by our senses. As a result of the quantitative way of seeing (Bortoft) nature is no longer understood to be peopled by beings but is the manifestation of forces and physical processes lying beneath their manifestation to our senses. The Human *being* has also now largely disappeared from view and is at best an epiphenomenon of genetics and complex biological processes.

superconscious and super-sensible[24] aspects of both consciousness and the phenomena encountered in nature. In fact, as highlighted by Brady, this science has even taken leave of its senses and embarks on a pseudo-empiricism, dealing as it does with phenomena that are not accessible to the unaided senses.

The implications are striking, for the way we experience the world, the way we engage with the world, the way we do science, the way we educate, the way we develop our agriculture, in short—the way we live—is informed by this *epistemology of separation*. It leaves us with the sense that we are separate 'subjects' faced with a world of separate objects... parts all...fragments of a wholeness that is no longer immediately accessible to the consciousness *which posited them as such*. Manipulation of parts (or pigs) is the inevitable result.

Kühlewind sums up the above conundrum in the statement "Science has been established on a level of consciousness where it cannot be adequate to the reality of Nature and the human Being" (1993, p. 5).

∞

The study of *ways of knowing* undertaken by Brady, Bortoft and others highlights one further very significant fact, crucial when considering the roots of the development of the science of modified organisms or the biodynamic preparations. This essential consideration is that ways of knowing the world change over time in quite fundamental ways. "There is always a non-empirical determining factor which is of cultural-historical origin. It is by recognizing this historical conditionality of scientific knowledge that we can be free from the enchantment with science which turns it into an ideology."

This recognition of the 'historicity' of science is incredibly significant for the study of biodynamics. It points to the distinct possibility

---

24. This term is used very broadly at this point to refer to those activities or beings who were—up until the Enlightenment—understood to be creative presences within the unfolding of the visible or sense-perceptible world. The Temple of the Winds in Athens, depicting eight wind gods, is an example of an earlier consciousness for whom the manifest (winds) were the sense perceptible clothing or activity of *beings* who were not perceptible directly to the bodily senses.

that biodynamics is neither a relic of an ancient way of knowing, long outmoded, nor is it a development in science that *can merely* be understood or grasped through the analytic and largely mechanistic science developed over the last centuries.

Bortoft makes a statement, arising from many years of studying the way in which J.W. Goethe pursued scientific research, which states this insight quite succinctly.[25]

I believe that a major obstacle standing in the way of our understanding of Goethe's alternative approach to the science of nature, is that we have an inadequate understanding of the way that mainstream science developed historically. As a consequence, we have several misconceptions about science, and fail to realize that the direction taken by modern science is only *one possibility*. In the beginning there are always more possibilities than the one actually taken. The choice which is made opens the door into the way that is followed, but at the same time it closes the door to other possibilities, which consequently withdraw into the background and are no longer noticed. They become invisible, but they do not cease to exist, and the time will come when unexpected consequences of the choice that was made, will begin to redirect attention to other possibilities that were not taken."[26]

Un-developed possibilities for paths toward an understanding of nature?

What might some of these paths be?

Could they point to a science 'adequate to the reality of Nature and the Human Being?'

And could they contribute to an understanding of the odd practice of placing plants in animal organs and burying them in the ground for a season?

---

25. Though Bortoft is making the statement in particular reference to Goethean science, I propose that his insight can be extended broadly to apply to non-conventional approaches to science more generally.

26. Henri Bortoft. *Taking Appearances Seriously*, p. 28

3
The Dance of Dandelions

"But it doesn't change..."

Exact Imaginative Cognition

We can readily find this plant—it is Taraxacum, the dandelion. The innocent, yellow dandelion is a tremendous asset…(it) is really a kind of messenger from heaven.

Rudolf Steiner, Agriculture

Seen one dandelion, seen 'em all…

…at least, this is what I bring with me on the morning that I decide to go out and pull dandelions from my garden beds where they seem to have sprung up like jack-in-the-boxes out of previously weed-free soil.

Like most plants, dandelions don't stand out from the crowd until they burst into bloom—or, rather, for the kind of attention that I usually have to spare… 'getting from here to there…' they register only as 'green' or 'plant' along with the rest of the leafy mass that surrounds me in the lush summer vegetation of the Cotswolds. That is, of course, until they bloom.

However, it must be said that even when they begin to unfurl their un-mistakeable yellow crowns, these plants are only registered in a blink—i.e. as 'unthreatening' or 'unexceptional'—and they are not spared a great deal more attention. Once named, our every-day attention usually moves on from such a generalized, quick-but-unconscious-identification way of seeing to the matter at hand—whatever non-dandelion event that might be.

Reaching down to pull out the 'invaders' from my garden beds... I sense through my hand for either that strangely satisfying feeling of a root letting go deep down at its tip, or the more irksome snap of a root left underground, half in—half out... poised to sprout, hydra-like, as soon as I move off...one more... three more...five more...

A pull and... 'sliiiick!'—un-earthed, roots and all!

Holding an uprooted culprit in my hand, satisfyingly dislodged down to the full extent of the tapering root tip, I am struck by the realization that I have never really seen a dandelion before!

Of course...I have looked at them, named them, pulled them up by the hundreds, blown their seed-clocks into the wind, played the game of 'head popped off' with my children...but I have not really seen them before.

I take a longer look, shift my attention from looking to trying to see...

I am soon sitting, garden fork laid flat, surrounded by the in-audible thrum of green things growing, all the world gone out of mind and sight save for a dandelion.

∞

Modes of consciousness

Analytical and abstract thinking has a certain pride of place in our contemporary world. This is of course essential as this mode of thinking or consciousness ensures that we get the bills paid, get to work on time, or sort out a *Quercus robur* from a *Quercus alba*. It is the case, however, that an analytical and often abstract way of knowing has become more and more prevalent in shaping both the individual and society, and not necessarily because it is superior to other ways of knowing (though it is of course often presented in this way). This ever increasing reliance on an abstract and analytical approach to knowledge is due instead to the pride of place it is given in our social institutions and activities.[27] The dominance of the analytical or 'verbal-intellectual' mode of consciousness, as described by Bortoft and others, is a product of developments in consciousness that have occurred over time, shaping both individual and collective ways of knowing.[28] The hallmark of this mode of consciousness is that it plays a crucial role in ordering and structuring our experience of the world and does so with a particular attention to the differences between perceptible details of whatever it is that we are perceiving.

∞

Looking at the dandelion, I am captivated by the tight whorl of leaves and the long tapering tap root. I am struck by the thought; How do I know it is a dandelion?

Several other plants, on closer inspection, also produce tap roots, and have leaves that hug the ground in a whorl of green.

Well, of course, it is the shape of the leaf that—in absence of any flowers—gives the game away (and the name away!).

My eyes follow the shape of the uppermost leaves, and I am taken by the spade-like leaf tip that emerges from a deeply toothed margin, 'teeth' that make the leaves so distinctive and gained them their common name of 'lion's teeth.'

Botanists have of course developed a very precise and specialist language for the identification of plants, based on the form, arrangement and number of different plant organs. I find myself trying the 'botanists way of seeing' on for size.

First off, this is no mere dandelion but—officially—bears the calling card Taraxacum officionalis.

---

27. "There is now a growing body of evidence to support the view that there are two major modes of human consciousness which are complementary. In our technical-scientific culture we have specialized in the development of *only one of these modes,* to which our educational system is geared almost exclusively. This is the analytical mode of consciousness, which develops in conjunction with our experience of perceiving and manipulating solid bodies." (Bortoft, 1996, p. 61)

28. See *The Master and his Emissary* by Iain McGilchrist (Yale, 2012). McGilchrist discusses two contrasting modes of attention' throughout this significant study of neurology, philosophy, and the development of consciousness.

Leaves: lobed (lobate to be more precise), toothed. Attached at the base (basal).

Stem: no visible stem. Instead the leaves grow out of a common point and form a rosette, close to the soil layer.

Root: Deeply tap rooted. Some lateral roots though clearly a dominance of the central tap root.

Exudes a milky sap if broken.

Flower: Flowering stalk (which I later learn is a 'scape') is produced in second year of growth. It is leafless. Hollow. Also produces a milky sap (latex) if broken.

Each leafless flower stalk culminates in a flower head which, upon closer inspection, comprises innumerable small flowers ('florets,' botanically speaking). The flowers are open during the day and closed at night.

Seed:The flower head eventually opens to reveal a spherical arrangement of seeds (achenes) with long stalks (beaks!) leading to feathery ends (pappus).

These are called 'clocks' by some.

The dandelion seeds, with their feathery pappi, are taken by the wind and may be deposited a significant distance from the parent plant.

This then is an abbreviated version of the dandelion anatomized by my attention to identify its separate parts (with a little help from the experts!). It is based on giving attention to the physically observable features of the plant.

It is also undertaken as a series of 'snapshots' of the plant—with a macro lens, zoomed in on specific parts. This way of seeing engages the plant as a static object, an arrangement of distinct parts. It is classification consciousness, driven by the question 'what is different?'

Engaging with this way of seeing is a strange process as it both takes me closer to the plant, on the one hand—I am aware of more detail than I had been previously while on my mission to pull the plants out of the garden—but, on the other hand, I am also oddly more distant. I have now a stronger impression of the different parts of Taraxacum officionalis *and even of the botanists' lexicon, but am not sure that such dissection would keep me enthralled for long.*

∞

A 'verbal-intellectual' way of knowing and the methods that derive from its development have inarguably contributed to many aspects of our knowledge and understanding. There is increasing attention, however, on the potential one-sidedness of this mode of consciousness and a number of studies highlight the imbalances that arise if this mode does not also find its complement.[29] One such study that has already contributed greatly to these considerations is *The Wholeness of Nature* by Henri Bortoft. In this very accessible study, Bortoft presents clear descriptions and arguments for a deeper understanding and engagement with scientific methods such as those developed by Johann Wolfgang von Goethe. Goethe describes his method as being firmly situated in the cultivation of "exact sensorial imagination" and Bortoft explores, at some length, the way in which Goethe makes evident a 'way of seeing' complementary to the 'verbal-intellectual' mode and—through examples of Goethe's scientific studies—reveals several of the features of this mode of consciousness. Imagination, in the sense used by Goethe, is no 'flight of fancy' or 'make-believe' but is a capacity for a way of knowing with deep significance.

Goethe is becoming increasingly well known for his studies of plants and of color phenomena and his mode of science is finding a renewed interest—particularly where there is a realization that the verbal-intellectual mode of consciousness cannot be the only instigator or arbiter of knowledge.[30] A challenge presents itself, of course, with this attention to the method of 'exact sensorial imagination' for the term (and activity) *imagination* needs some clarifying. Imagination is—in the sense being used here—an activity of consciousness which takes focus, inner commitment and repeated engagement in order to develop a new way of seeing the phenomena of nature in terms of '*becomings*' rather than '*things*,' activities rather than static objects. Whereas the verbal-intellectual mind separates, objectifies and delineates, the holistic mode of conscious engaged in the cultivation of imaginative ways of knowing relates, animates, and intuits connections. In *It All Turns on Affection*

---

29. Again, it is worth acknowledging Iain McGilchrist's contribution to this theme in *The Master and the Emissary.*

30. See *Goethe's Way of Science*, edited by Arthur Zajonc and published by SUNY press.

Wendell Berry articulates his own use of the term 'imagination' in the following:

> The term 'imagination' in what I take to be its truest sense refers to a mental faculty that some people have used and thought about with the utmost seriousness. The sense of the verb 'to imagine' contains the full richness of the verb 'to see.' To imagine is to see most clearly, familiarly, and understandingly with the eyes, but also to see inwardly, with the 'mind's eye.' It is to see, not passively, but with a force of vision and even visionary force. To take it seriously we must give up at once any notion that imagination is disconnected from reality or truth or knowledge. It has nothing to do either with clever imitation of appearances or with 'dreaming up.'

∞

Still holding the dandelion in hand I shift my attention into a different way of seeing. Up until now I have been looking at the dandelion. Now I begin to enter more fluidly into the way in which the dandelion has grown. I begin to imagine the dandelion growing from a seed to the point where I now hold it as a plant with a mature rosette and well formed tap-root, and then continue on into the formation of flowers.

The dandelion has, after all, not just appeared here overnight, each subsequent stage dropped in by some night crew not seen but implied by the daily differences observed in the plant.

The plant is an unfolding in time, and not only a material presence in space. To try and get closer to this way of seeing the plant—as a becoming—I start to shift my attention into how the dandelion has grown.

Accompanying this growth inwardly, through an imaginative recapitulation of its actual development in time, I attempt to plunge into dandelion-as-verb, instead of my usual habitual treatment of it as a noun.

Attempting to capture this growth-in-time with pencil and paper, I end up with a very different representation than those that emerged from my previous engagement. This way of seeing has more the quality of a time-lapse image than that of a static snapshot.

Through this line-dance, the dandelion reveals a very particular dynamic.

The first year's investment in the forming of the rosette, with a concurrent downward growth of the taproot, gives a strong impression of 'holding back' or 'restraining' of the vertical growth (in other plants often manifest as a stem extending skyward, with leaves spaced out along its vertical length). Whereas other plants clearly demonstrate an elongation in the vertical (heliotropism) from the start, dandelion seems to hold to the earth, and—rooting strongly—even be directed earthwards.

This is at least the case for the first year.

In the second year a very different drama unfolds. The opposite to the first year.

A kind of explosive growth unfolds skywards.

Flower stalks shoot out vertically, at times to remarkable heights in relation to the ground-hugging rosette. In fact the dandelion somehow seems to accommodate its surroundings and manages to extend this flowering head just above surrounding herbs and plants, into the airy space above it's neighbors. Here it undergoes a series of expansion and contractions synchronized with the daylight, before forming its 'clock.'

Finally the familiar seed heads, complete with feathery pappus, are taken by the wind, almost 'given' to the wind is my impression, and—airborne—defy the initial earthwardly oriented root with an expansive flight limited only by the strength of wind.

I recently came across a book by biologist Craig Holdrege[31] in which he writes; "the plant is a teacher of dynamism, prodding us to look beyond fixity to transformation." I now feel, through dancing with the dandelion, that this description captures very well what is happening for me as I shift from looking at the dandelion to looking with Dandelion.

It is now no longer just a 'plant' identified with a glance (and pulled up with a tug) but is more of a dynamic, a living organism with a particular way of going about its life process in the great symphony of the plant world.

∞

In contrast to the verbal-intellectual mode of consciousness which serves to distinguish and isolate, the *holistic mode* described by Bortoft allows for a meaningful synthesis to emerge out of the products generated by the activity of the analytical mind. This new synthesis or perception of meaningful wholeness is different from that which the verbal-intellectual is able to produce because it arises from a fundamentally different mode of consciousness. It is, as Goethe demonstrated

---

31. *Thinking Like A Plant*

in his work, suited to gaining insight into the realms of *life* and *dynamic relatedness* where the intellect has excelled in revealing the laws of the inorganic. This mode of consciousness has been referred to by various names, such as 'holistic,' 'integrative' or 'synthetic.' It is described by Bortoft as:

> nonlinear, simultaneous, intuitive instead of verbal-intellectual, and concerned more with relationships than with the discrete elements that are related. It is important to realize that this mode of consciousness is a way of seeing, and as such it can only be experienced in its own terms. In particular, it cannot be understood by the verbal-intellectual mind because this functions in the analytical mode of consciousness, for which it is not possible to appreciate adequately what it means to say that a relationship can be experienced as something real in itself. In the analytical mode of consciousness it is the elements which are related that stand out in experience, compared with which the relationship is but a shadowy abstraction. The experience of relationship as such is only possible through a transformation from a piecemeal way of thought to a simultaneous perception of the whole. Such a transformation amounts to a restructuring of consciousness itself. (1996, p. 63)

Whereas the verbal-intellectual mind is suited to perceiving and manipulating solid bodies, the holistic mind, through the cultivation of the imagination, can begin to intuit the meaningful relationships intrinsic to the realms of life.

The potential for imaginative cognition for illuminating aspects of natural phenomena inaccessible to the verbal-intellectual mind is exemplified by the Romantic poets—Goethe, Novalis, and Coleridge are but a few examples—who saw a "spontaneous, sober observation of the world"[32] as essential to their work. These poets were often very deeply engaged in the study of natural phenomena—Novalis in

---

32. Allison, 2003, p. 14

mineralogy, Goethe in botany and color phenomena. They, also, in distinction from other natural scientists, turned to artistic modes of expression (poetry, literature) in order to relate their insights in such a way as to weave together understanding of natural phenomena with a deeply penetrating search for the meaning for these insights as they relate to human life and development. Through a deep investment in the sense life and in phenomena as revealed to the un-mediated senses, accompanied by a cultivation of an imaginative way of knowing, the very opposite of the demotion of direct experience described by Brady is revealed.

∞

Dandelions

What's in a name?

I have been digging again—but this time into the motley field of common names for our seemingly common dandelion.

The name we are most used to calling it comes from the french 'dent-de-lion,' referring to the toothed leaves. This name arises from physical features of the plant.

Other names spring from a similar source—blowball, blow-flower (Pusteblume), doon-head-clock.

Some names indicate an association or link with the human world—witch's gowan, monks-head, priest's crown.

Still other names derive from the dandelions medicinal uses, effects it has on the human body and in relation to the human physiology—cankerwort, pissenlit, wet-a-bed—names that begin to indicate its actions when ingested in the human body (diuretic).

These latter names begin to speak to a further dimension of dandelion that arises as we start to become more familiar with its gesture, it's modus-operandi, its way of being. It is a being!

This is particularly the case with names based on what it does, how it does, who it is that does.....

Whereas in my weed-picking point of view it was only necessary that I came to the overgrown garden with an identification consciousness—this be a dandelion, this be not—in the shift of consciousness to a more fluid gaze I engaged with the time-process, the 'how' of the dandelion. In the phenomena of a name a still more intimate relationship arises as the nature of naming (at least in its deeper sense) is rooted in the question 'who are you?'.

This 'who' now begins to shine 'through' the physically observable aspects of the dandelion that I first observed. Dandelion is not merely the leaves, flowers, seeds as drawn above—these are the footprints of the dandelion left in passing. Dandelion is a dynamic, whose clothing is at one time leaf (and rosette), at another root, now, flower, now seed...

"The plant lives in the cosmos and dies in the meadow."[33]

∞

Along with the heightening of perception through an investment of attention in our sense life, the development of imagination in the sense proposed above also re-orients awareness toward the superconscious pole of consciousness. It places awareness back in touch with the living, dynamic source and seat of both consciousness and organic growth, and loosens the rigidity of the subject-object separation, which arises due to the gradual orientation to, and identification of consciousness with, the products of its activity—its past.

Once we come to recognize *both modes of consciousness,* the analytical and holistic ways of knowing, these can be cultivated consciously and developed complementarily. A way of knowing that embraces both the analytical prowess of the intellectual mind with a concurrent cultivation of the dynamic vitality of an imaginative intelligence ensures that our way of knowing stays in touch with the realms of life, and in so doing informs a way of living adequate to Nature and the Human Being.

∞

---

33. A phrase I attribute to Dennis Klocek.

Dandelion
(alias 'GoBetween')

Earthbound
traveller alights
extends root into
earth, bores down, down
condensing light from toothed whorl
above. Persistence, patience, awaiting sun's full
circle overhead...—The turning!—Spring flush and thrust
of growth, hollow stalk crowned golden, splayed,
displayed, crests the green sward, echoes
suns' systole, diastole, once...twice
...thrice—unfurls filigree globe
all feathered, wind gift
'Swept aloft—at
last!' reborn
skywards

∞

'New Solutions' Revisited

Now for a bit of a 'stock take'... Where has a journey into epistemology, modes of consciousness, and dandelions brought us?

This journey began, after all, with the specific questions of how to understand the thinking that led to a genetically modified pig, on one hand, and a mixture of plant and animal substance brought together to enhance compost on the other.

Questions of epistemology led to the exploration of ways of seeing and modes of consciousness which revealed a shift from a 'piecemeal' way of seeing to a dynamic engagement with a plant as a becoming, a being. How does this meeting with dandelion contribute to the question that launched this whole study in the first place?

It is now possible to look once again at both the Enviropig and the Oak Bark preparation and to consider further the types of thinking or ways of knowing that contributed to their creation.

Craig Holdrege, in his article "The Gene: A Needed Revolution," articulates from a number of references the dominant role that the verbal-intellectual (and analytical) mode of consciousness has played in informing much of the early thinking about genetics that has given rise to the genetic modification of organisms. The reduction of complex bio-logical organisms to the functional units of clearly identifiable, and thus transferable "genes" arises from "a mechanistic model of the gene and of gene action that inaugurated the age of molecular biology." This per-spective is not held only by biologists or specialists in genetics but is widespread:

> Most people today are familiar with the term "gene" and have
> learned in school and through the media that genes determine
> the characteristics of organisms. There are genes for hair and eye
> color, genes that direct the formation of our body's substances, and
> many genes that are somehow defective and cause disabilities and
> illnesses—genes for diabetes, cancer, schizophrenia, and more. No
> one talks about human, animal or plant physiology today without
> ascribing a central role to genes. (Holdrege, 2005. p. 14)

Holdrege refers to the gene described above as the "deterministic gene" (p.15) and states that the way of seeing this "gene" as a key to "de-ciphering the mechanism of life…lives in the minds of many students, lay people and—at least as a desire—in the minds of many biologists" (p.15). This is the same type of consciousness encountered—and critiqued—by Brady in *Being on Earth*. The reductive tendencies of the verbal–intel-lectual mind, which reduce (in the above example) life to 'mechanisms' governed by distinct and identifiable 'genes' lies as the main focus of the many criticisms that have been brought to bear in considerations of the appropriateness (or otherwise) of the genetic modification of organ-isms.[34] These critiques are relevant to a consideration of the Enviropig.

---

34. See for instance *GMO Myths and Truths,* available at www.earthopensource.org

From this perspective it is but a further reduction that follows the initial abstraction of the pig from its natural environment.[35] The Enviropig, in light of the above, arises from the analytical, reductive, and mechanistic modes of thinking characteristic of the verbal–intellectual mode of consciousness. It is an illustration of the tendency for this mode of consciousness to give primacy to 'parts' and to view organisms as complex mechanisms with a degree of inter-changeability of those parts. This way of seeing, as I encountered in my meeting with dandelion, places emphasis on the difference or distinction between the separate parts and from this perspective ('looking at') an intrinsic connection between the parts is overlooked or denied. A new 'synthesis' is possible, from this perspective, by the re-arrangement or re-combination of parts (such as 'genes') in order to create a new whole with more 'desirable' traits. Such virtuosity with 'components' in the creation of a new organism has given rise to many critics of this approach dubbing this new porcine breed the 'Frankenpig,' and grave doubts are expressed by its opponents regarding the ethical and appropriateness of this slight of hand with generating new organisms in this manner.

In light of the above considerations—and contrasted to the phenomena of the Oak Bark preparation, maybe the question is not just if the new creation or synthesis is appropriate or 'right,' but if more attention needs to be placed on the initial act of separation.

The need to explore the process of 'separation' does, in fact, present itself when we consider the biodynamic preparations once again, for here the choice of 'parts' is not so evident.

---

35. I am not going to undertake an exhaustive critique of the Enviropig as this has been undertaken by others. Suffice it to say that on closer examination, the initial problem of overly phosphate rich effluent from pigs and the potential pollution hazard that ensues has more to do with the ways in which the pigs are raised -(so called intensive or factory farming), the type of feed they are given (grains high in phosphate which would not normally be consumed by pigs and certainly not in the quantity given in feedlots) and the fact that they are removed from ecological relationships in which their faeces would be naturally processed and incorporated by other organisms, plants etc -than to do with the pigs themselves. For more on this perspective of the issues raised by the modification of what is now the Enviropig see http://howtoeliminatepain.com/ibs/enviropigs

Clearly there is a type of abstraction or separation evident in this example as well. The skull was once part of a living being, the oak bark is separated off from the tree on which it has grown, the two are placed in the ground in contact with flowing water. But on what basis were they chosen—*separated out*—from other plants, or animal organs? Is this a random act of separation or is there a meaningful relation informing this choice? What mode of consciousness or method of mind lies behind this separation, and might insight into this question also lead to more light being shed on the subsequent synthesis?

Rudolf Steiner provides in his Agriculture Course an indication for a kind of thinking and way of science that may provide a meaningful context for first 'separating out' of these substances prior to bringing them together again in the 'new synthesis' of the biodynamic preparation: "there is a hidden alchemy in the organic process. This hidden alchemy really transmutes the potash, for example, into nitrogen, provided only that the potash is working properly in the organic process"(Steiner, 1993, p.102).

Now, as Brady encountered in his pursuit of a science rooted in direct experience, alchemy is not often viewed by scientists of today with any *current* or contemporary relevance. It would be easy to dismiss Steiner's phrase referring to a "hidden alchemy" as either a convenient metaphor or to take this statement as further grounds for rejecting Steiner's proposals as 'unscientific.'

Does he really mean alchemy?

4

Encountering Alchemy

"People wonder about what you are pursuing..."

Alchemist following Natura/Wisdom
by M. Maier, Atalanta Fugiens, 1618[36]

Art, Science and the Sacred

Journal Entry:
August 30th, 2007
Prague, Czech Republic

Had dinner at an Italian restaurant overlooking the city. Monasteries, embassies, a beautiful orchard with ripe fruit falling off the trees.

I am the only diner on a broad terrace overlooking the whole of Prague and the Vltava river.

Rain moves in great grey bands over the scene before me, interspersed with the odd shaft of sunlight that finds a way through the cloud cover.

Having spent the day on a walking tour of the city, it is good to now be an onlooker over the streets and buildings to which I have only just been introduced. My mind is filled with a jumble of thoughts and images, arising from a day spent tracing the history of alchemy and alchemists through time, and through Prague. Accounts of Emperor Rudolph II and his interest (and overt support) for esoteric research jostle with names…John Dee… Michael Maier… Edward Kelly… and the search for the philosopher's stone.

Had my first introduction to that not-oft used word (or deed!) defenestration. (Thankfully not at first-hand.)

∞

---

36. *'Nature, Reason, Experience and Reading must be the Guide, Staff, Spectacles and Lamp to him that is employed in Chemical Affairs.'* Nature here is portrayed as the woman bearing fruit & flowers, and Reason is the pilgrim's staff, Experience his spectacles, and Literature his light.

Until quite recently, modern accounts of alchemy were quick to place it as a pseudo-science that preceded the later and—it might by suggested—more 'rational' and 'objective' science of analytical chemistry. Chemistry, from this point of view, emerged into the light and clarity of precise knowledge through the Enlightenment, leaving behind the murky and mysterious practice of the alchemists with their ambiguous texts, images, and confounding terminology. "From the very beginnings of 'the Divine Art' of alchemy, its esoteric practitioners used every known device of cryptic expression, allegory, mystic and symbolic representation in order to 'vaile their secrets with mistie speech'."[37]

Historians of science often contrasted the "quiescence and stagnation" of a pre-Enlightenment science of alchemy with the "spectacular advances in heralding the approach of a new age" that marked the dawn of 18th century analytical chemistry. In John Read's account we can thus find one example of a view of alchemy which paints it as the soil (dark and somewhat dirty) out of which there "blossomed" the modern science of chemistry. The chemist and historian of science Lawrence M. Principe writes the following regarding this view of alchemy in his book *The Secrets of Alchemy*;

> The repudiation of transmutational alchemy by the professionalizing discipline of chemistry was reinforced by broader trends during the period generally known as the Enlightenment (roughly the eighteenth century). Alchemy became one of the many foils writers of the era used to enhance the achievements of their own age and to distinguish it from everything else that came before. Enlightenment rhetoric was full of stark polarities—of light replacing darkness, reason supplanting superstition, new thinking casting out old habits. It dealt analogously with the new binary of chemistry and alchemy: modern, rational useful chemistry supplanted archaic and misguided alchemy. (p. 89)

---

37. John Read, *From Alchemy to Chemistry* p.40

Chemistry was referred to in its early days as *Die Scheidekunst,* that is 'the art of separating.' This is perhaps surprising, given our contemporary distinction between the disciplines of art and science, but it contains within it a faint (and dying?) echo of the fact that Alchemy was known as the Royal Art—a theme which will be explored at greater length in what follows. Delving deeper into the development of the science of chemistry we find that it is indeed a story of the innovation of ever more refined ways of separating the 'stuff of the world' which gave rise to ever changing views of the nature of the 'stuff' in the process. This is no simple story or one that is recapitulated easily in a short space, but it encapsulates the shift from a view of 'matter' (Mater, the 'mother') rooted in the Four Element theory of the ancient Greeks, through the recognition of the composite nature of Air (by Van Helmont, Lavoisier, and others) to the development of spectroscopy and ever more refined (and technologically rooted) modes of 'analyzing' substances. The result is the widely familiar periodic table of the elements and the quantification of the discrete elements conceived as the building blocks of the world in which we find ourselves (and the bodies through which we experience that world). The guiding inspiration in pursuing this path of ever greater reduction and quantitative analysis has been that we will, in the process of getting to the 'roots' of what constitutes 'matter,' come closer to what makes up the dynamic world in which we find ourselves. From some other points of view, however, the way we have gone about this great separation has left us holding only the *corpse* of nature (of *Mater*)—the life having been bled out of her as soon as we started to dissect and analyze with a view to 'looking inside' to see what made her tick.

> If you want to know and describe what lives,
> Seek first to drive the spirit out,
> Then you will have all parts in hand,
> Having lost, how sad, the spiritual band.[38]
>
> Goethe, *Faust*

---

38. Wer will etwas Lebendiges erkennen und beschreiben,
    Sucht erst den Geist herauszutreiben,
    Dann hat er die Teile in seiner Hand,
    Fehlt leider nur das geistige Band.

∞

I'm am not sure what it was about the brochure that first caught my attention and awoke in me the wish to take part in the proposed 'Quest.'

In part it was of course the evocative cover... bordered by an image of Goethe , the figure Alchemia, and several artistic renditions of Weimar and Marienbad. It was certainly inviting enough for me to delve into the text that followed... "a unique conference that will travel from the medieval silver mining town of Kutná Hora, an hour east of Prague, to the pearl of Bohemian spas, Marianske Lazne (Marienbad) and conclude in the evocative and beautiful Thuringian town of Weimar, home of the great German poet, playwright, novelist and scientist, Johann Wolfgang von Goethe." The clincher, particularly due to a growing interest in morphology and a curiosity for one of its main proponents was the sentence: "Our quest will be to follow the Western Esoteric Tradition from sixteenth century Bohemia to its reemergence in Goethe's artistic and scientific work. And throughout we will ponder the special spiritual gift that this tradition offers to the contemporary world."

Alchemy? Contemporary world?
Art and science?
Well it was all too much to pass off and I bought my ticket for an Esoteric Quest in Central Europe, run by the New York Open Center.

∞

A view of science is described by the mathematician George Adams that paints a rather different picture than that often presented, i.e. of a neat linear development of pre-Enlightenment ('pre-rational') sciences giving way to the clear, objective sciences of the modern era. "The history of science is not the unidirectional process which neatly finished textbooks lead one to suppose. Many streams run side by side, the most essential discoveries, experimental or theoretical, may lie unnoticed for decades till a fresh aspect emerges to reveal their importance." (*Potentisation and the Peripheral Forces of Nature*).

In a 'unidirectional process' of science depicted as follows...

...we are asked to imagine a progression from antiquity (left side of the line) through the philosophical flowering of the Greek period, the medieval period of alchemy and 'pseudo-science' to the pivotal period of the Enlightenment and on into our present age of post-Enlightenment clarity and objectivity of a rational science that is just within reach of the God particle.

In contrast, Adams proposes a more varied story, and one that is more and more convincing when attention is placed on the *ongoing* streams of a variety of approaches to the study of the 'stuff' of nature.

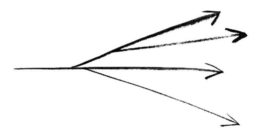

Alchemy is, from this point of view, one of these streams or branches that has run throughout the history of science and natural philosophy from antiquity right up into the twenty-first century!

It is even becoming increasingly well known that many scientists and thinkers who are hailed as the fathers of modern analytic and materialistic science were, in their day, engaged in a rigorous and life-long pursuit of studies in the Hermetic tradition. Newton, Boyle, Locke ... these are but a few of the esteemed scientists who studied and corresponded with like-minded individuals in the sciences around matters alchemical. As uncomfortable as this may be for proponents of a 'unidirectional' interpretation of science, it seems that these individuals invested significant time and energy in a path of knowledge that only became discredited in time when approaches to science shifted to favor more materialistic ways of seeing.

Alchemy, it begins to become clear, is not just the pre-cursor to a later scientific development (and one that was supplanted in the process) but is *another* path of study, another *way of knowing*, and one that is very current. The lamp of alchemy burns on!

∞

August 31st, Kutna Hora

Visited the alchemy museum in the morning. Some interesting alembics and vessels shaped like stomachs and other organ-like forms. Went down a silver mine in the afternoon, hard-hatted and in miners garb—a pair of overalls and head lamp.

In the evening we listened to a concert in an old rectory—included a rare chance to hear Atlanta Fugiens by Michael Maier played by virtuoso Czech musicians! Awe inspiring.

September 1st, Czech Republic

Attended various lectures held in a grand old palace or stately home in the countryside some miles from Kutna Hora. Various scholarly combings through the 'role of Bohemia in the Rosicrucian tradition,' the life of Jacob Boehme, and the history of Kutna Hora. Visited the Sedlec Ossuary on the way back to the town. Estimated to contain the skeletons of between 40,000 and 70,000 people. A bizarre and admittedly macabre afternoon stop-over. Hard to comprehend. Due to the deft hand and creative panache of a woodcarver named Frantisek Rint the overwhelming presence of death is quirkily offset by skeletal chandeliers, coats of arms, and other ornamental uses of human bones.

Not at all sure what to make of it.

Afternoon lecture on Heinrich Khunrath: Amphitheatrum Sapientiae Aeternae. Fascinating!

∞

A very engaging way to approach the question 'what is alchemy?' and to get a glimpse of what alchemists were engaged with in their 'Royal Art' is to study an alchemical emblem.

Reproduced here is an image from the work of Heinrich Khunrath, a physician, hermetic philosopher and alchemist from the 16th century. At first glance it is perhaps a jumbled image with a seemingly random assortment of elements and is evidently not representational of an actual room or space. The image, rather, offers a succinct description—in image form—of those elements deemed necessary by Khunrath and alchemists of the time for progress on the path of knowledge. The emblem is thus, if we can 'read' the image accurately, a way to access an approach or method for a science ('way of knowing') that preceded the more analytic and quantitative science which followed.

The emblem clearly delineates three primary activities or areas to be addressed. In brief, we find a depiction of the tri-unity or mutual relation between three distinct disciplines: *spiritual practice,* the *study of natural phenomena,* and *art.*

Various interpretations of the Khunrath emblem have been proposed. Alexander Roob in his book *Alchemy and Mysticism* gives the following caption for the image: "We can awake […] through constant prayer in the oratorium (left), and through unstinting work in the laboratorium (right), which rests on the two pillars of experience and reason. The oven in the foreground admonishes us to patience, and the gifts on the table remind us that sacred music and harmony are supposed to accompany and define the Work" (Roob, 2001, p. 331).

Peter Forshaw, whose doctoral dissertation centered around a study of Khunrath's *Amphitheatrum sapientae aeternae*,[39] brings to this study a wealth of knowledge which reveals the multiple layers of meaning embedded in this fascinating image. These layers arise from a multitude of influences informing the alchemical opus—including Christian-Cabala, practical laboratory work, and a long lineage of esoteric study and research. Images are used in combination with text—note the Greek, Hebrew, and Latin phrases sprinkled liberally throughout the emblem.

Although images such as this are complex and reveal multiple layers of meaning through repeated study, I have come to understand Khunrath's emblem in the following way.

It was understood by the natural philosopher engaged in alchemical pursuits that our insights come via "grace." We can work, strive, question, and pursue knowledge of the world though we must at all times be aware that our knowledge arises through a moment of grace—it is, in this sense, a 'gift.'[40] Thus a conscious, contemplative attitude is essential in order to cultivate the receptivity and reverence that are prerequisites of the work. This is in fact the first step in the alchemical practice, made explicit in the meta-structure of Khunrath's emblem which illustrates the alchemical mantra *ora, lege, lege, lege, relege et labora*, notably with *ora* preceding the other two endeavors. This guiding idea is depicted in many alchemical emblems and texts, being something of a universal mantra that informs the alchemist's work. It translates as *pray, read (or study), read, read, re-read, and work*. Khunrath's emblem is filled with guiding admonitions, short but poignant phrases directing the alchemical seeker toward knowledge and understanding (and that ever enigmatic Philosopher's Stone).

---

39. See Forshaw, Peter (2005) *Alchemy in the Amphitheatre: Some Consideration of the Alchemical content of the Engravings in Heinrich Khunrath's Amphitheatre of Eternal Wisdom (1609)*

40. Kühlewind's articulation of the superconscious and its role in the formation of both everyday consciousness and scientific consciousness (both of which function on the same "plane," though differ in intensity) touches on a similar insight regarding the processes of cognition. Insight, from this perspective, arises from the superconscious as grace—a received gift.

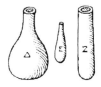 *Dormiens vigila—while sleeping, keep watch*[41]

The Work begins in the Oratory (pictured on the left of the emblematic space in Khunrath's image), with the alchemist kneeling in a reverent gesture. The text in the oratory is a constant reminder that *SINE AFFLATU DIUINO NEMO UNQUAM UIR MAGNUS—NO ONE IS EVER A GREAT MAN WITHOUT DIVINE INSPIRATION.* Working in the laboratory (to the right hand side in Khunrath's emblem), between the pillars of experience (experientia) and reason (ratio), we investigate the mysteries of nature. Referred to as a whole as 'the Art,' the hermetic methodology included the instruments of expression (depicted as musical instruments in the center of the amphitheatrum emblem), expression both of insights derived from the Work and of the divine harmonies informing Nature's creative unfolding—the Harmony of the Spheres. This emblem is thus an epistemological process made visible, comprising three mutually interpenetrating activities each with its own "laws," methods, and materials, all interlinked and inter-dependent in the search for knowledge.

 *Festine Lente — make haste slowly*

In Khunrath's emblem I suggest that a way of knowing is articulated which embodies an integrity that was subsequently fragmented and lost owing to changes in human consciousness. This change represents a massive chapter in the history of ideas; I have referred to this in several passages of this book. The approach to science articulated by Brady in

41. All translations for text quoted from the Khunrath emblem are courtesy of Dr. Peter Forshaw, Assistant Professor for History of Western Esotericism in the Early Modern Period, Center for History of Hermetic Philosophy and Related Currents, University of Amsterdam

Being on Earth has, in this light, grown out of the fragmentation of the relationships depicted by Khunrath.

Today, the disciplines of the artist and the scientist are still all too often viewed as being *separate* and incongruent in method and intent.[42]

If we were to draw Khunrath's image as a depiction of the relation of these disciplines in a modern sense, we would need to isolate the three elements into quite separate compartments (or departments!). They would have to lie within their own frames, having been largely defined as distinct disciplines. Fragmented and compartmentalized, science, the spiritual life (including religion), and the arts have been relegated to different quarters, and it has been science that has claimed the authoritative voice in questions of truth and certainty.[43] This science, severed as it has been from the earlier recognition of the necessity of engaging the superconscious through contemplative practice and prayer, has become inimical to these realms.

Sapientae retentatum, sucedet aliquando
— wisely tried again, it will at length succeed.

When I first encountered this image and the methodology it articulated, I felt that here was an epistemology and a method that held within it certain key principles. It asked of the individual student of Nature and of the Human being three very important questions:

1) What is your study/research?
2) What is your art?
3) Do you cultivate a conscious connection to the spiritual
   (or superconscious) source of both of these?

---

42. Goethe is a clear example of a scientist/artist who made significant contribution to both fields of human endeavor but who is largely given credit and respected for either his artistic works or his scientific method, but rarely both.

43. It was my meeting with this attitude in the Town Hall meeting that struck me as an affront to other ways of knowing besides the reductive, analytical, quantitative and largely mechanistic stance that underlies much of contemporary scientific enquiry.

Through *study*, by which I mean science in its commonly understood sense, as well as in the sense of the study of the insights of other researchers, we can develop our thinking and cognitive capacities. I would also emphasize the crucial activity of epistemological self-reflection in this realm, as any act of consciousness is subject to the dynamics that have been explored above through the work of Brady, Bortoft, and Kühlewind.

Through the *arts*, we both bring to expression something of our own personal experience and strive to lift this personal experience to the level of what is universally human.

Through the *spiritual life,* I understand this to mean both a contemplative method with regard to our subject matter as well as a conscious attitude of mind and heart that is cultivated when we apply ourselves in either of the aforementioned ways. As physicist Arthur Zajonc has described so clearly in his article "Love and Knowledge" (2006), a contemplative methodology in the sense meant here includes and seeks to cultivate an ethical stance both to one's science and one's art. It is the contemplative method and practice which places our work on an ethical ground and ensures that it doesn't get caught in the traps of either an objective, impersonal, and "value-free" science which becomes antithetical to life,[44] or an artistic practice which merely embellishes the subjective, personal and egoistic life of the individual.

NON PUDEAT CARBONUM
— DO NOT BE ASHAMED OF COALS

In Heinrich Khunrath's depiction of the hermetic path of knowledge there lies an indication of a way of knowing which may be adequate to understanding Nature and the Human Being. This way of knowing engages and honors the disciplines of science, art, and contemplative practice, each in their own right—in 'separation' as it were—while also

---

44. "Surely, science has brought enormous advances, but we cannot turn away from the central fact that the modern emphasis on objectification predisposes us to an instrumental and manipulative way of being in the world." (Zajonc, 2008, p. 3)

recognizing that for the student of nature to continue in any of the three disciplines *in isolation from the others* would lead to one-sided knowledge of Self and World.

It was in a *right distinction* followed by a *re-integration* of science, art, and the spiritual life that the way to knowledge was assured. This attention to right separation and right synthesis lay at the very root or foundation of the alchemical world view, encapsulated in one of the most often quoted aphorisms in the alchemical opus—*solve et coagula, et habebis magisterium*. From the perspective of the 16th-century alchemist this way of knowing mirrored processes in the laboratory, in living organisms, in the natural world as a whole.

 *Disce bene mori — learn to die well*

Now, at this point, you may be wondering what all of this alchemical theory has to do with biodynamic preparations, skulls, bark, and stag bladders stuffed with yarrow flowers?

A brief recapitulation:

In my encounter with the Enviropig it became clear that a type of logic was being applied in its creation which was very familiar to me, though somehow I had the sense that this logic—applied to the *living realm*—was misplaced. It became clear to me that the Enviropig derived from a type of thinking —'the logic of solids'— that arose from the study of the inorganic realms of nature. This thinking can only work piecemeal, treating parts of organisms interchangeably but with no under-standing of the organism as a *living being.*

Undertaking a study of the dandelion through a method inspired by J. W. Goethe, I realized that it is possible to enhance the 'onlooker' approach to the study of natural phenomena with a way of seeing that gradually reveals the dynamic, metamorphic nature of living organ-isms. This touches into a *participatory way of seeing,* in which a very new relationship to the organism—dandelion—emerges. This moves the initial analytical way of seeing to a more contemplative way of seeing. It shifts the subject (or object?) of study from being an 'it' to a 'thou.'

The comment by Steiner regarding 'a hidden alchemy,' given in the context of the first indications for the biodynamic preparations, along with my encounters with the historical and philosophical roots of western esotericism in Eastern Europe led me to turn my atten-tion to the study of alchemy—initially from a theoretical perspect-ive. This was undertaken through a study of alchemical imagery and ideas encapsulated in them. The themes of 'right separation' and 'right synthesis' emerge from a study of Khunrath as central tenets in an alchemical approach to knowledge of Nature. The importance of this insight goes well beyond a mere theoretical interest or exploration. In order to grasp the significance of the polarity of 'right separating' and 'right synthesis' with regard to biodynamics and preparation making (and further developments in science generally), a fruitful direction for further study presented itself to me in the work of one of the most colorful and enigmatic figures of medieval alchemy—Philippus Aure-olus Theophrastus Bombastus von Hohenheim, known more widely as Paracelsus.

Often referred to as the 'father of *spagyrics*,' or plant alchemy, Paracelsus developed medicinal preparations for his work as a physician through a *practical alchemical* application of the theoretical approach outlined by Khunrath. In doing so he followed the guiding principle of the alchem-ists: *solve et coagula et habebis magisterium!*

5

Separate, Purify, and Recombine

.

"You have to explain about the thread..."

Spagyrics—Solve; separation

September 2013

It is a day poised between summer and autumn. Cool enough to warrant a fire in the workshop, but a warm hint in the air makes the outer layer of wool donned this morning seem excessive.

A day for distillation.

Two days ago, at Gables Farm just outside Nailsworth, Gloucestershire, I spent a blissful two hours harvesting peppermint. Bright sun on my back, full bed of dark green leaves jutting out from rod-like purple stalks, blush of blossom, flush of scent, cumulus cushions overhead, light breeze passing through…

Now back in the workshop the comforting crackle and warmth from the wood fire couples with the burble and drip from the still and the air fills with the scent of peppermint set free.

My alembic is an old pressure cooker, bought from a second-hand shop and altered to take a pipe-fitting purchased from a plumbing supply store. A motley, but supremely effective sequence of glassware gathers the steam rising through the mint and channels it up and over into a Leibig condenser fitted vertically. Cooled with gravity-fed water from a rain barrel behind the workshop, the whole set-up is simple and low tech … but rather elegant!

The simplicity of the distillation apparatus belies the wonder that always arises from this ancient Art. A herb steamed in a closed vessel, the vapor captured and condensed and—hey presto!—the essential oil separated from the host plant, floating atop a richly scented hydrosol (or herbal water).

The alchemist calls this process the separating of the 'soul' of the plant from its 'body,' and obtains in the process the volatile oil, or 'sulphur principle' of the plant being distilled.

To make the process even more precise, I have included in the distillation train a separator to allow for a good separation of oil from water. Here the oil col-

lects on one side, unable to pass through the apparatus, while the water droplets fall through an ever increasing oil layer to eventually run off into a receiver on the other side. It is in this separator that the real wonder and magic of this simple act of distillation is revealed.

Two liquids, but of very different natures, separate—the one floats upon the other. The essential—volatile—oil above, and the catalyst for its release—water—below. Water and oil.

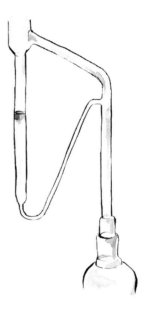

As the essential oil layer increases during the distillation, perfectly spherical water drops travel down through this layer, gathering toward the bottom like clusters of clear grapes before dispersing into the watery depths below.

This mesmerizing layer of water and oil contains within it a whole host of images and ideas that informed the alchemical understanding of nature and substance—the volatile and the fixed, the sulphur and the mercury, the cosmic and the earthly—and it is this layer of oil that I watch keenly as more and more peppermint goes into the pot!

After about an hour, I am feeling distinctly light headed from a room filled with the uplifting scent, and a satisfying 6ml of oil has been collected in the separating funnel. Sensing that the mint in the pressure cooker is now 'spent,' I turn the heating element off, detach the still head, and open the pressure cooker. The originally dark green leaves have turned into a washed out, greenish-brown, flaccid pulp which is tipped into a fermentation bucket.

I take some fresh handfuls of peppermint, chop them up with a herb knife and re-fill the pressure cooker. Setting all the glassware back in place and turning on the heat, I sit back to observe and contemplate this deceptively simple act of separation…

The process begins again—the essential from the non-essential!

∞

Alchemy has had a long association with agriculture. Manfred Junius, author of a significant book on plant alchemy writes; " the old masters recommend that we always follow Nature and let her do the work of her own, *like a farmer.* The closeness of alchemy to agriculture has often been emphasized, and there were alchemists who assumed the nickname 'Agricola'" (Junius, p. 18). Robert Allen Bartlett writes "alchemy has been described by many of the ancient masters as a sort of 'Celestial Agriculture.'" Thus it seemed to me that a hands-on engagement with practical alchemy would likely be a fruitful avenue for shedding light on Steiner's statement that a 'hidden alchemy' informed organic processes—processes of transformation—in the plant and soil. This, at any rate, was the hunch that guided me toward the study of plant alchemy. I undertook this not only to educate myself in the practical procedures and work with plants, but also to study the way in which my inner life of thoughts, feelings, and reactions was influenced by undertaking the more 'outer' processes in the lab. In this way the study of plant alchemy—or *spagyrics*—offered itself to me as a bridge between the study of matter and mind –between 'knowing' and 'doing.'

Practical Procedures

*The vast field of spagyrics presents itself …
like a mosaic that is only slowly completed by
the collaboration of the reader.*
— *Manfred Junius*

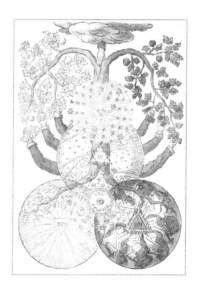

An excellent 'guide book' for my forays into plant alchemy came to me with yet another enigmatic alchemical emblem on its cover.

Six arms clothed in red reach up to pick apples from the limbs of a tree, the arms emerging from behind three interlocking spheres adorned with an array of symbols...

all very intriguing and evoking the impression that I was about to step back in time, into the smoky and dimly lit labs depicted in so many illustrations of the alchemical path.

The book in question, *Spagyrics: The Alchemical Preparation of Medicinal Essences, Tinctures and Elixirs,* is however a book of the twentieth century, and not a resurrected manuscript from the heyday of fifteenth century alchemy. Manfred Junius, the author of the book, was (until his death in 2004) very active as a pharmacist, plant alchemist[45] and a very modern thinker. Junius gives the following succinct introduction to the spagyric process in the following passage:

> In the word *spagyrics* two Greek words are hidden: *spao,* to draw out, to divide; and *ageiro,* to gather, to bind, to join. These two concepts form the foundation of every genuine alchemical work, hence the often quoted phrase *"solve et coagula, et habebis magisterium!"* (Dissolve and bind and you have the magistery). The alchemical work always takes place in three stages: (1) separation, (2) purification, (3) cohobation (recombination, or the "chymical wedding").
> (Junius, 2007, p. 1)

With this excellent guide book in hand, I set out to make an alchemical herbal essence, following in particular the process as outlined by Junius in Chapter 5 of his book titled "The extraction of the three Philosophical Principles from Plants."

Solve — separation and purification

First separation: volatile oils

"A large number of medicinal plants contain a considerable amount of essential oils. Especially rich in volatile Sulfur is the family of the labiates (Labiatae). In this family, compromising about three thousand species, which directly represents the prototype of the family of medicinal plants—all its species are medicinal—we

---

45. The practice of spagyrics is undertaken currently by many individuals and in several fully licensed spagyric pharmacies worldwide, see for instance SOLUNA laboratories and Phylak laboratories.

find our known favourites: rosemary, the mints, basil, balm, which are everywhere easily available. If we cultivate these plants in our garden, we can considerably increase their content in volatile Sulfur by giving them a proper neighbourhood of other plants, for example, by planting them together with stinging nettles."
(*Ibid.*, p. 60)

I chose three plants to work with: mint (*Mentha spicata*), sage (*Salvia officionalis*), and lavender (*Lavandula augustifolia*). The plants were harvested in bulk from different locations, chosen for their vigor and optimum harvest time. This was determined by their state of flowering or growth as the plants maximize their essential oil production at different times of year and in different plant organs (flowers in the case of lavender, leaves in the case of mint and sage).

I separated the parts of the plant containing the greatest concentration of essential oils from the main plant body (i.e. leaves for mint, flowers for lavender) and put these into a distillation vessel to obtain the essential oils through steam distillation.

Plant matter not processed through distillation was put to one side.

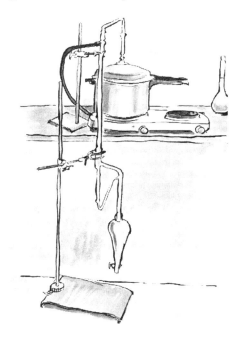

I adapted a large pressure cooker with a pipe fitting to distill in bulk, used a glass reduction adaptor to link the pressure cooker to the glass still head and condenser. A separating funnel positioned below the condenser allowed for a very precise collection of essential oils and separation of the floral waters. In the subsequent distillations I obtained 15ml of mint oil, 20 ml of sage oil and 50 ml of lavender oil.

These were each labelled and stored in brown glass bottles.

Second Separation: Fire water!

"After the drawing off of the essential oils, the remaining plant 'soup' is subjected to fermentation. In the fermentation container we find the Four Elements. The plants together with the sugar are the Element Earth. The Element Water is also present. The Element Air is released in the form of a gas (carbon dioxide). The Element Fire can be recognized by the liberation of heat energy during fermentation. In the midst of these four Elements alcohol develops, which, however, is not identical with any of the Elements. This is our Mercury, which is therefore sometimes also designated as Quinta Essentia. An often-heard alchemical theorem is: The Quinta Essentia is none of the Four but proves to be one of the Three (Philosophical Principles)."

(Ibid., p. 70)

All of the plant matter—that from which the essential oils was removed (mainly leaves) as well as stems, stalks, even roots set aside before distillation—were placed in a fermentation vessel. Water was added to the vessel as well as grape sugar[46] and wine yeast. The vessel was fitted with a lid or cork with an air lock. The vessel was kept in a room with a steady temperature of around 20-25 degrees Celsius.

At this temperature the fermentation proceeded at a constant rate. Once the fermentation was complete (noted through a cessation in the production of gas and the sinking of the plant matter to the bottom of the vessel) I separated the liquids from the solid matter through a fine filter.

The plant matter was set aside to dry. The plant 'wine' was then ready for *rectification*.

---

46. Junius states that the addition of grape sugar "is permitted since Mercury is the same in the whole plant world." (Junius, 2007, p. 69) I will return to this designation of alcohol as 'Mercury' in subsequent sections. In brief, Mercury refers not to the grape sugar but to the alcohol obtained from the conversion of the grape sugar.

Rectification: Separating water from wine

I struggled with this process for some time.

It is no wonder that the alchemists of old devoted much time and effort to mastering the art of distillation. Their objective was not to obtain fine 'spirits' for pleasurable consumption (though no doubt the skills, technique and apparatus developed by alchemists served the development of the brewer's and distiller's craft) but rather to 'rectify' or 'purify' the 'Spirit' of the plant matter which was obtained in part when the plant 'gave up the ghost' in the process of fermentation. Junius describes at length various methods and contraptions developed for distillation (of various substances) and provides many illustrations of classical distillation set-ups.

The process provided several challenges for me, a truly novice spagyricist. The indications to distil at 78°C caused a lot of frustration as it would either proceed incredibly slowly or I would get overly concerned with watching the thermometer, and panicking a little every time the temperature went up into the 80s.

In the end however, I realized that it is the *repeated* distillation that is crucial and that by working initially with higher temperatures the gradual purification—*rectification*—of the wine could be achieved. I also became intrigued, and increasingly aware, of the fact that—for an alchemist—it was not the purity alone which was being cultivated in this repeated process in a chemical sense, but rather a *qualitative* change accompanied the repeated procedure. This is perhaps a good time to look at how the old Masters viewed the Art of repeated distillation, and its purpose.

"Now I am come to the arts, and I shall begin from Distillation, an invention of later times, a wonderful thing, to be praised beyond the power of man, not that which the vulgar and unskillful man may use. For they do but corrupt and destroy what is good. But that which is done by skillful artists. This admirable art, teaches how to make spirits, and sublime gross

bodies, and how to condense, and make spirits become gross bodies. And to draw forth of plants, minerals, stones and jewels, the strength of them, that are involved and overwhelmed with great bulk, lying hid, as it were, in their chests. And to make them more pure, and thin, and more noble, as not being content with their common condition, and so lift them as high as heaven."
—*Jean Baptiste Dela Porta, (1600)*

It is clear that practical procedures had a multi-layered meaning for the alchemical practitioner, and that along with the separation of one substance from another, there was a purification and 'ennoblement' of the substance in the process. Potentially, at least!

Third separation: soluble salts

"Our now-dry plant residues are first reduced to ash in a flameproof dish, and the ash is subsequently calcined. After this the water-soluble salts are separated from those that are insoluble in water through extraction with distilled water. We obtain a white, strongly hygroscopic salt (the Salt proper), and a certain amount of light grey Caput Mortuum. We preserve both substances in closed glasses." (Junius, 2007, p. 91)

This process presented some further challenges. It was difficult to get a good combustion of the plant matter and obtain the ash. Eventually I discovered that the wood-fired bread oven that my family and I had built in our garden was the perfect incinerating oven. I fired the oven in such a way as to ensure that the fire—positioned at the back of the oven—produced abundant flame that licked out over the oven bed and then emerged out the oven door. Plants were incinerated separately (i.e. all the lavender incinerated and the ash collected prior to the incineration of the sage, or mint). Plant matter was placed on large baking tray and, when placed in the oven, produced copious amounts of grey smoke before bursting into flame. Plant matter was added until all of the leaves, stalks, and stems from each of the three plants was turned to ash. The ash was then left in the hot oven for several hours. It was a very dramatic process, and took several hours of tending the fire to ensure a complete combustion of the herbs. The reduction of plant matter to ash was also remarkable, as several large bagfuls of herb would reduce to a cupful of ash.

The subsequent extraction of the salts from the ash was largely straightforward, though there was much learned from doing it. The desired result of the process is "a white, strongly hygroscopic salt" (*Ibid.*, p. 91). When I took the salt solution off the ash using a soxhlet extractor, the resulting liquid was an amber, tea-colored solution. The salts that were left after evaporation of the water were also orange-brown in color. This, according to Junius, is not pure enough and needed subsequent calcinations and purifying.

These salts went back into the crucible, back into the oven and the process of calcination, dissolution, filtering, and evaporation repeated. This took some patience and commitment to repeating such a time-intensive process, and asked for a greater amount of diligence in the next round to ensure a thorough calcination.

With the sage and lavender I made sure that the initial incineration and calcination were more thorough, undertaken in intense heat and sustained exposure to that heat in the bread oven. The salts of these plants, once obtained in the same method as described above, were white.

And so I completed the first half of the alchemical *solve et coagula*.

Viewed pictorially (below) the process, though described as a step-wise sequence of laboratory procedures—can be viewed in its entirety. This is described as a *separation* from a primal unity (the plant as we encounter it in nature—alchemically a 'Mixta') into three 'essential' principles, the subsequent purification of these principles before their eventual re-combination or cohobation in a process of *coagula*. Thus far I had only undertaken (and described) the first stages of the process—the *solve* and purification stages.

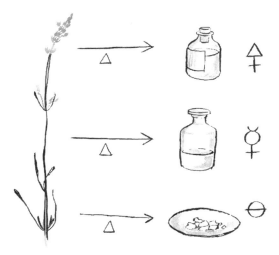

Three From One

This first stage in the work of *spagyrics* revealed several significant 'fruits.' The three substances that are 'separated out' from the initial plant 'unity' have strikingly different characteristics. I was amazed that such different substances derive from the same original plant 'body.'

Essential Oil — Sulf — 🜍

The essential oil has a distinctive scent, completely unique to each plant species, and even more so, to each group of plants. This distinctive aroma encapsulated in the essential oil, or volatile oil, is immediately recognizable. The oil itself is flammable, will not mix with water (which allows for its separation from the plant body through steam distillation and simple separation methods) and dissipates readily in normal temperatures and conditions. Essential oils can be a variety of colors—from the deep blue of chamomile oil to the red of cedarwood oil, the golden yellow of several citrus oils to the clear and colorless oils of pine, rosemary, mint. Essential oils are, alchemically, substances that strongly emphasize the *sulf* principle in their formation and action in the plant realm.

Salts — Sal —

The salts obtained from the plant manifest properties polar opposite to those of the essential oils. They are obtained through the fact that they *will* dissolve in water, but will reappear out of solution once the water is evaporated off. The salts crystallize out into very distinctive, often geometric, forms. They are odorless, will not burn, melt only under very high heat (in the region of 900° C) and are strongly alkaline. The salts are, ideally, white or clear and highly hydroscopic once obtained. The salts, alchemically, image the *sal* principle in the plant/mineral realm.

Alcohol — Mercur —

Between these two quite polarized substances arises the alcohol. Whereas the essential oils are unique to every plant species, the alcohol is the same —ethanol— regardless from which plant it is obtained. This characteristic earns it the designation 'anonymous' from the spagyric perspective, in distinction to the 'specific' nature of the essential oils. Junius writes, "ethyl alcohol is an easily combustible, clear, colorless liquid, simultaneously fire, water and air" (2007, p. 55). The alcohol is, alchemically, a manifestation of the *mercur* principle in the plant realm.

The alcohol, positioned between the oily volatility of the essential oil pole, and the earthy, crystalline nature of the salt pole, is the perfect picture of a mediator (*mercur*). Where the oil won't mix with water, and the salt won't 'burn' or become 'volatile,' they will both dissolve in the 'firewater' (alcohol) and 're-unite' as an essence or spagyric tincture—3 in 1.

This initial phase of the spagyric process, *solve,* did not aim toward — or result in— an analysis of the plant into its chemical constituents (carbon, hydrogen, and oxygen, for instance) but rather to the point where three qualitatively different substances were obtained. Separation—in spagyric terms—thus is evidently an act of *differentiation without a loss of distinction* or distinctive quality. This is one of many striking realizations that emerge from an engagement with this practical alchemical work.

Bridging the Gap

Now, not a lot has been described thus far that could not sit comfortably in a standard chemical laboratory, or be defined in analytical chemistry terms. *Solve* is, after all, an 'analytic' process—separating out discrete components or elements from a former compound, complex, or amalgam of substances.

However, in order to draw out and make evident a shift between a purely analytic and 'objective' process and the more 'participatory' nature of alchemical ways of knowing, I would like to revisit two aspects of the spagyric 'solve' described above.

The first regards the nature of 'heat,' and the other the substance 'salt.' Both of these aspects took on new meaning through a practical immersion in the spagyric process, and came to have direct relevance to my central question regarding the biodynamic preparations and the nature of the 'synthesis' proposed by Steiner in the creation of these new catalysts for the transformation of substance and self.

6

Dragons and Hens

"But it is hard for others to see..."

Qualities of heat

" What we call 'hot' seems to be immortal and to apprehend all things:to see and hear and know all things, both present and future. This otherness, then, the diversity of the all, when things become clouded, went out to the furthermost revolution, and seems to me to have been what was called ether by the men of old."
— Heraclitus[47]

NEC TEMERE, NEC TIMIDE –

NEITHER RASHLY, NOR TIMIDLY

I have included in the diagram on page 106—between the plant and each of the three substances obtained through the process of 'solve'—the small symbol Δ.

On the one hand, this symbol represents 'fire' or 'heat,' as it is through the application of heat in various forms that the processes of separation and purification take place (for instance distillation—a 'moist heat,' fermentation, calcinations).

47. from *Remembering Heraclitus*, Richard Geldard (2000), p. 97

It is through my work with the spagyric process, that this seemingly obvious catalyst for all of the laboratory processes described here gained a new significance, which in turn 'opened' up my understanding of various other aspects of the work. In order to make evident this new *way of seeing* 'heat,' I will briefly revisit the spagyric process.

∞

It is now late autumn. A good time for burning.

Two bottles sit upon the shelf in the workshop, awaiting a third.
In one bottle rest the results of taking two big bags of peppermint through the distillation process; a cool clear 15 ml of peppermint oil.
In its neighboring bottle, 500ml of 'rectified spirits of mint.'

For the first step of the spagyric preparation to be completed—the solve—I need now to obtain the soluble salts.
I gather the mint leaves that have been through the fermentation process and give these an initial drying in the now empty greenhouse. The low autumnal sun is still giving out enough heat to warm up this small glass house, and it makes for a good drying space.

Once the plant matter has dried a while I undertake one of my favorite late-autumn activities—lighting the bread oven which stands in the garden behind the house.
I make a fire of well seasoned oak wood.
Once the fire is burning intensely, I push the coals and still-burning logs to the back of the oven. There is no chimney on the oven—or rather the chimney has been blocked off—so the combustion process proceeds through a draw of air in through the open doorway of the oven at floor level and the flames lick up and over the inside of the oven in a slow mesmerizing dance. Just before putting a tray of herbs in the entrance to the oven, I add a good handful of smaller oak branches to the fire in order to ensure that the flames produced come fully over the oven bed and out the of the oven door.

I then insert a tray full of dried mint plants into this inferno—ducking down in order to push the tray into the oven (and to avoid being blasted in a plume of heat)... not too close to the burning oak at the back, but well under the arch of flames that roll out of the oven... and wait, standing back to observe.

The herbs begin to smoke profusely and crackle before bursting into flame. Out of the oven door bursts an intense heat and thick clouds of billowing smoke. Slowly mint stems and leaves disintegrate, turning first to a blackened mass which gradually gives way to glowing shards of red embers. These drop and disintegrate finally into ash in the tray bottom.

I continue with this radical fire-work until the entire herb is incinerated—another great reduction, the original large bags of mint plants giving rise to a few cupfuls of formless, grey ash.

It is exhilarating to work with this intensity of heat and fire, and not without its risks. A singed eyebrow and the odd minor finger burn are part and parcel of the incineration process. Working with fire in this manner really gives the strong impression of working with a force of nature requiring careful handling, like an animal or being of some sort with a will of its own.

Fire demands respect.

'Handling' fire means understanding its idiosyncrasies—it needs 'feeding' on the one hand, and 'tending' on the other. We must accommodate ourselves to its ways, understand how it will behave in a set of given circumstances, and provide the right conditions for it if we are seeking to harness fire's creative—and destructive—potentials.

After the initial burn a grey ash is left covering the bottom of the tray.

I leave this in the oven exposed to the heat of the fire and coals that last for an hour or more, baking the ash further.

I then take the ash, cool it, place it in a glass beaker and pour distilled water over the ash to fill two-thirds of a beaker.

After twenty-four hours, I pour this solution of ash and water through a paper coffee filter and obtain a clear salt solution in the process..

Holding in mind indications from Junius' good guide book, I know that what I need to do next is to evaporate the water off in order to obtain the salt crystals. In this process my thoughts run along a pretty pragmatic route—efficiency and speed will be the thing!

I put the solution in an evaporating flask and place the flask on top of a wood-burning stove.

Rapid evaporation ensues.

A crust of salt forms on the surface of the solution and creates a skin over the top of the remaining solution slowing down the evaporation. Though I know in my mind that I am aiming for a 'crystallization' I become quite fixated on obtaining a dry matter in the dish. The salts are so hygroscopic, so 'thirsty,' that if they are not exposed to heat there is always a wet solution in the dish. I grow impatient and on the next firing of the bread oven, put the evaporating dish in the entrance to the oven once the firing has settled down a bit. In this way I am able to get a dry salt—but it is a crust, not crystallized out but baked onto the evaporating dish. A moonscape, not a 'crystal heaven!'

For days I struggle with the process of evaporation, feeling more and more frustrated and increasingly impatient—seeking for the formation of good, distinct crystals out of the salt solution. I oscillate between heat sources that are too gentle, too intense or too intermittent.

What on earth am I doing wrong!?

∞

As in many cases, the solution (!) to problems we encounter when trying to 'solve' their chaotic and ungraspable complexity is only achieved when (or if) we manage to overcome the way in which the problem is being approached. We need to shift *ourselves*, how *we* are engaging with the problem.

In retrospect, it is easy for me to see what I needed to do. I had forgotten, perhaps, that I needed to keep an 'open mind' and that insights (or solutions) are not squeezed out of the matter at hand through our own will and determination but that they often arise as a 'gift' or grace into a more 'listening' consciousness. The history of science is full of accounts of insights that arise after the scientist has shifted attention from the focussed and directed efforts in the lab, to the more dreamy, open consciousness freed up by a bath, a walk, or some other catalyst for an opened mind.

Just such a shift was facilitated for me by a trip away for a few days, and by getting some distance from the process.

A Gatwick moment

As I was returning from a trip abroad, standing in the customs queue in Gatwick airport, I had the following experience.

Having ample time to get either frustrated or impatient (three hundred people were being served by a handful of immigration officers). I chose instead to reflect on the process I had been working with. I had recently described the process to a colleague and explained that I was looking for a certain type of heat—not temperature but more of a quality and specific *condition* of heat...

Standing in the queue I was running the process through my mind as a series of inner pictures, when the image of the tray of herbs lying in the bread oven came to mind...

herbs engulfed in flames from the intense heat...

a plume of flames from the burning oak logs at the back of the oven licking out the door of the oven...

The following image suddenly popped into my mind; and with it came an insight as to the meaning of two particular figures in the image, the exactness of the figures in *qualitative* meaning, as well as insight into the process required to obtain the crystallization I was seeking.

To be specific, what came to mind was the image of the dragon on the left side of the emblem and the hen sitting in a basket on a clutch of eggs, lower down and to the right.

I first came across the image several years ago in *The Seer's Handbook* by Dennis Klocek. Though I had not studied this image for some time, it arose in my mind while I was standing in the queue in Gatwick and the following insight accompanied the arising of the image.

Dragon and hen were here depicting two different qualities of heat.

MONS PHILOSOPHORUM.

By qualities I mean not just temperature, degrees Centigrade or Fahrenheit, but the *conditions of heat*. Furthermore, these spoke not only of 'external' qualities of heat but they crossed the boundaries of the 'outer' phenomena—measurable in degrees—to the 'inner' nature of heat that I had encountered in the process of obtaining the salts. I have referred to these as 'exhilaration,' 'impatience,' and 'enthusiasm.'

The images of dragon and hen became dynamic, bridging *meanings*—uniting the previous dichotomy of 'outer' process and 'inner' understanding and, in the process, I realized the solution to my problem.

The dragon instantly spoke to me of the intensity of the combustion process, the smell of singed hair and choking carbon-rich smoke, of the ferocity of the flames as they consumed the dried herbs, of the sweat and determination it took to tend the fire with poker and glove. Dragon heat—I realized—is indiscriminate, used to 'incinerate' and leave nothing in its wake. It is a fierce heat and requires determination inwardly to work to these temperatures. It is only barely contained and unfolds in a tricky balance between encouraging it to be its hottest and most destructive (like 'goading' the dragon out of its cave) and nonetheless contained in order to consume only what is offered up to it.

Hen heat, on the other hand, is the picture of a constant, unchanging heat, 'brooding' warmth that knows that the process can't be rushed. The hen is the picture of patience, self-sacrifice even—an exact image and foil to my own impatience in wanting to rush the crystallization process, a process that, after all, requires in nature the conditions of constancy and extended time. The image was not just—in the moment of its arising—a picture depicting an external process, but was at one and the same time an admonition for me to be 'hen-like' in allowing the crystallization to take its course. I realized that I had not yet found the means to adequately produce this type of heat. Here was an intensification of my realization of the significance given to *qualities* of heat in the alchemical texts. Heat expanded as a concept to include elements of time, intensity, exposure, duration (direct flames, residual heat from heated stone, gas flame, electric element…) and came to include and embrace the inner nature of my own 'heat' (impatience, intensity, concentration) *as well as* the outer nature of heat (constant, enveloping, radiant) in a unified experience.

At the same time as realizing a greater depth to the phenomena of 'heat' in the processes I had been undertaking in the lab, the sense—or understanding—also shifted profoundly for me of the beings themselves, in their embodied reality.

Dragons are hard to come by, but hens—on the other hand—are seen daily outside my window. Hen as a 'bird' became for me an embodiment of a particular relationship to heat, to warmth—it was first and foremost a warmth-being, and its intrinsic warmth-nature became more significant than the feather and squawk creature present to my senses. The hen—positioned between the reptile and the early mammal in evolutionary terms—is a creature that has not yet internalized the warmth process completely, at least not in its reproductive cycle. The hen, having an externalized reproduction cycle in the stage of the egg, needs to 'brood' and incubate the egg with its own bodily warmth. Without the warmth of the mother, the insulation of the feathers and down and the bodily 'cavity' of the nest, the young will not mature and hatch. My perception/conception of the familiar physical phenomena of a hen changed and has remained altered since my encounter with the alchemical nature of 'heat.'

Salt—Sal

A similar shift in understanding arose for me regarding the nature of 'salt.' Prior to my experience with the spagyric process I had a rather static conception of the substance 'salt.' It was, I could say, a very concrete, material conception of a physical substance that—if not mechanically broken down and presented in the saltshaker for culinary use—was a building block, itself made of building blocks (Na, K, C, etc.). Through the struggle to obtain the salts as described above, my conception of salt shifted; whereas before it was 'stuff'—matter, inert—it subsequently has become more of an activity, a *dynamic*. Salt—in my mind—is a concept that encapsulates the *coming into being*, or *becoming* of the salt crystal—it includes the burning, dissolving, evaporating, crystallizing... Salt is not just the 'stuff,' it is more-than-manifest; it includes and encompasses its time in solution, evaporation, and slow accretion of form in stillness. Salt becomes 'stuff,' an abstract 'thing,' only when we undertake a 'solve' conceptually—when we separate out its becoming and only cognize its manifestation.[48]

Through the coalescence of experience (practical lab work), theory, living with a problem, and the encounter with the imaginal in the form of the alchemical image, I realized that the alchemist was not just using ambiguous images where words and numbers would suffice but that they rather used images from the natural world in an exact manner, derived from a "seeing the phenomena in depth"(Bortoft, 1996).

I was left with, and am still left with, a *dynamic* sense of heat, salt, the alchemical image, the 'essence' of the process and *myself* as collaborator in that process. This experience was one of touching the transformational potential of working with the different elements of the spagyric process—the substances, the practical procedures, the contemplative activity, the alchemical image... 'the making of the medicine is the medicine.'

All of this description belies the pains it takes to describe in words what was—standing in the queue in Gatwick—a split second insight, a timeless moment, revealing a correspondence of inner experience, image, and un-resolved questioning.[49] In the briefest of terms, I woke up to the fact that I was—in pursuing a crystallization of the salts—using dragon heat

---

48. That this is a *way of seeing* and not 'just the way it is' in a positivist sense is explored at some length by Bortoft in *The Wholeness of Nature* (1996). Salt perceived through the *quantitative way of seeing* is what I have described in this sentence. A new way of seeing, and a new perception of salt, opened up for me through the experiences described in the preceding section.

49. In his book *Thinking Like a Plant* (2013) Craig Holdrege references this experience, giving examples of it in the life and work of Thomas Kuhn and David Bohm. Bohm (p.85) refers to this 'flash of understanding' as *imaginative insight* or *creative imagination*. Holdrege draws attention to this experience as being analogous in plant development to the often striking, surprising even, arising of the flower out of the leafing process of the plant and offers the term *flowering insight* to describe this experience. (see Holdrege, *Thinking Like a Plant* pp. 83-86 for further discussion of this cognitive experience.)

where I should have been using hen heat. To achieve my aim I had to find a 'hen,' and some patience.[50]

The *Dynamics* in Biodynamics

Now, salt and heat do not have an apparent connection to the biodynamic preparations, and in particular not to the Oak Bark preparation, which is after all the catalyst for this journey into matter and mind. How has this research into spagyrics—or the initial process of *solve* at least—contributed to my understanding for bringing together plant material (oak bark), animal organs (skull) and specific indications for burying these combinations in the earth for designated lengths of time (over the winter)?

My Gatwick experience left me with a distinct and first hand experience of a different *mode of consciousness* or *way of seeing* that the alchemists had encoded into their emblems and that spoke both to the 'outer' work in the lab and the 'inner' world of the alchemist. In the alchemical emblem, aspects of 'the Work' that would appear unrelated from one way of seeing—salt crystals, hens, and the impatience (or patience!) of the operator—became united in a qualitative dimension, perceived through a shift in my mode of consciousness.

Approached through an imaginative consciousness, heat and salt—characterized alchemically as the polar principles *sulf* and *sal* along with the mediating principle of *mercur*—constitute a dynamic threefoldness—a three-in-one—that provides a window into processes and substances not accessible to a purely intellectual, analytical way of seeing.

The significant potential for an understanding of the processes *sal, sulf,* and *mercur* to contribute to the quest for a deeper understanding of Steiner's new alchemy are explored in the next chapter.

---

50. I am not suggesting that the 'meaning' of the dragon and hen that I gleaned from the image of the alchemical mountain is necessarily the meaning that the author intended. Images have many meanings, but for me the insight arose in such a way as to profoundly influence my sense of how warmth processes unfold in the phenomena of nature, and in the 'soul.'

7

Three-in-One

"While you hold it you can't get lost ..."

Thunder.
Enter the three Witches

First Witch
> *Thrice the brinded cat hath mew'd.*

Second Witch
> *Thrice and once the hedge-pig whined.*

Third Witch
> *Harpier cries 'Tis time, 'tis time!*

First Witch
> *Round about the cauldron go;*
> *In the poison'd entrails throw.*
> *Toad, that under cold stone*
> *Days and nights has thirty-one*
> *Swelter'd venom sleeping got,*
> *Boil thou first i' the charmed pot.*

ALL
> *Double, double toil and trouble;*
> *Fire burn, and cauldron bubble.*

> — William Shakespeare, *Macbeth, Act IV, Scene 1*

Tria Principia

It is no accident that the creative activity of the imagination has yielded the number three again and again—in stories and sacred texts, in fairy tales, in legends and in myths. Three bears, three wishes, three witches, three wise men, three sons, three chances… the list goes on and on. Something lies in this number three which is timeless and virtually universal, revealed in the literature of all cultures and ages.

Alchemically, we have encountered this *threeness* in the three Philosophical Principles—*sal, sulf,* and *mercur*. This triad of processes was deemed by the alchemists to lie at the root of all of nature's manifestations. They were seen to have a kind of universal significance, perceptible in the 'outwardly' visible beings and processes in nature as well as in those of consciousness, as revealed in the creative images that arise from its activity.

Manfred Junius writes:

> According to the alchemistic conception, the entire manifestation of matter is maintained through the cooperation of three Philosophical Principles, which are also called the Three Essentials or Three Substances.
>
> The different proportion of the three substances in the countless forms of manifestation of matter accounts for their multiplicity. For this reason, the various materially existing things are sometimes also called Mixta (mixtures). A metal, for instance, is a Mixtum, likewise a plant. In this way specific proportions of the Three Substances... form the basis to every chemical (or alchemical) element. The three Philosophical Principles form a unity in the triad, though they are different from one another. (2007, p. 29)

Junius here locates the three principles of *sal*, *sulf*, and *mercur* in the realm of the "manifestations of matter," i.e. in the realm most recently engaged with by the physical sciences. But is this indication that the three principles give rise to the multiplicity of 'the manifestations of matter' of any relevance today? It is for *spagyrics* and an alchemical worldview, but these pre-date our contemporary analytic and 'modern' science. Would it not be a mistake to bring alchemical thinking back into science?

I will say 'no,' it is not a mistake. In fact, quite the opposite. I will, in what follows, lay out a path guided by considerations of the Three Principles that will reveal the potential of this 'three-in-one' to take our understanding of the substances and beings we encounter in nature to a new level of meaning. For the principles *sal*, *sulf*, and *mercur* as we have encountered them in plant alchemy provide a new way of seeing the multiplicity of facts that derive from a contemporary analytic study of nature. The *Tria Principia* of the alchemists can be seen, in this light, to provide a 'key' or cipher for unlocking meaningful relationships otherwise hidden by a dominantly quantitative and reductive study of the natural world and the human being. The knack, however, is in grasping these three principles through *exact imagination* as dynamic *processes*—both distinct and inseparably, or rather *polarically*, related. Before introducing some of the examples of sciences which will illustrate this potential of the Tria Principia, and before building a bridge between these and biodynamics, a brief recapitulation will help set the scene.

Separating out—'Solve'

The spagyric process begins with 'separating out,' or the separation (*solve*—analysis) of three substances or 'Essentials' from a plant. These three essentials are referred to in a number of ways. They have terms that are familiar from a modern perspective of analytical chemistry—essential (or volatile) oil, alcohol (ethanol), and salt (potassium carbonate). They also have designations that originate in an alchemical perspective. Collectively they are referred to as the Tria Principia or Three Principles, although individually they are referred to by alchemists as the 'soul' (sulf), 'spirit' (mercur), and 'body' (sal) of the plant.

To be a bit more precise, the *sulf* principle in the plant (essential oil) is understood to be the 'seat of the soul' of the plant, the substance wherein the 'individuality' of the plant touches in and comes to clearest expression. The alcohol, likewise, is—not materially but as qualitative substance—the seat of the 'animating principle' (spirit or life spirit) of the plant. It is evident from these references that the Three Principles are—for the alchemist—far more than the material substances (essential oil, ethanol, potassium carbonate) with their clear chemical classification.[51]

---

51. To go back to its roots, the principles as we have encountered them in spagyrics are described in the following way by Paracelsus:

> *The body is developed from Sulphur, that is, the whole body is one Sulphur, and that a subtle Sulphur which burns and destroys invisibly. Blood is one Sulphur, flesh is another, the major organs another, the marrow another, and so on: and this Sulphur is volatile…Now the stiffening of the body comes from Salt: without the Salt no part of the body could grasped. From Salt the diamond receives its hard texture, iron its hardness, lead its soft texture, alabaster its softness, and so on. All stiffening or coagulation comes from Salt. There is therefore one Salt in the bones, another in the blood, another in the flesh, another in the brain, and so on. For as many as there are Sulphurs there are also Salts. The third substance of the body is Mercury; which is fluid. All parts of the body have their own fluid; thus the blood has one, the flesh another, the bones, the marrow, each has its own fluid , which is Mercury…Know then that all dissolution arises from these three.*

These are, in fact, only the precipitates or temporary dwellings of these three principles.

The alchemical terms are now added to the right of the drawing re-produced here:

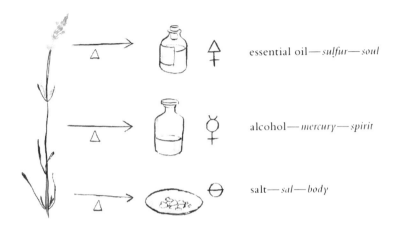

essential oil—*sulfur*—*soul*

alcohol—*mercury*—*spirit*

salt—*sal*—*body*

The Spagyric solve process. The alchemical terms for the Tria Principia are in italics.

Arising out of the process of *solve,* the essential oil, alcohol, and salt are very different substances, and if their origins in the body or unity of the plant from which they are derived is forgotten or ignored, the three substances seem to have little in common or have little to relate them each to the other. A loss of *meaningful relationship* can in fact arise in any study wherein the products of analysis lose touch with a principle that reveals their inherent relationships.

There can be, for instance, clear distinctions made between the chemical elements silica and calcium based on an analysis of their physical properties. When placed in the periodic table of the elements, these physical properties clearly define the place of these two elements in a schema derived from weights and measures but nothing is revealed thereby of the roles that these two elements play in the *unfolding of living beings.* Nothing indicates that compounds of these elements ($SiO2$ and $CaCO2$ in particular) play an important and complementary role in a myriad of organic processes in the living world. A different 'lens' is needed to grasp the *dynamics* of silica and calcium (and of other elements), and scientists are—in several instances—finding such a lens in the Tria Principia.

Let's now turn to concrete examples of scientists who are re-engaging with the Three Principles in various fields. It is important throughout the following to maintain an active, *imaginative*, contemplation of the dynamics revealed through approaches to natural scientific studies which set out from a renewed contemplation of the *Tria Principia*.

∞

Tria Principia: Perspectives

What better place to begin this contemplation of the three-in-one than in the study of chemistry!

For here we are putting our attention (aren't we?) on a science which emerged *out of* alchemy into quantification and systematization and which, in the process, purged itself of earlier 'mystical' influences. An alchemical study of chemistry… a contradiction in terms?

Chemical Contemplation

It will be difficult to find the connection between the human being and nature if we don't know this Principle, since we are an actual ordered expression of the Three Principles.   — *F. Julius*

Teacher and chemist Fritz Julius, author of *Fundamentals for A Phenomenological Study of Chemistry* (2000), takes up the Tria Principia in the following description;

Salt signifies crystallization processes, as well as everything that involves condensation and hardening of substance, and especially points to the transition between the liquid and solid state.

Mercury symbolizes everything that is mobile interaction, in transformative activity, and especially the manifold matter cycles with their play of condensation and evaporation, as represented especially by water.

Sulfur exemplifies the process of burning, and also processes in which warmth arises and matter disappears.

If a person earnestly contemplates such thoughts, they will experience that thoughts like these can contribute a great deal towards forming a grand, imaginative picture of the whole of nature. (p. 18)

Julius proposes an approach to the teaching and study of chemistry that can (as the alchemical world view did in its way) establish a relationship to *life,* to living processes, and to the human being. He does so through a re-engagement with the Tria Principia. Julius further illustrates the *dynamic* view of chemistry that he seeks to establish in the following passage headed "Chemistry as an Intermediary between an Organic and Inorganic Science."

If we say: a chemical element can participate in a sequence of metamorphoses, then that is not correct. The element itself is a metamorphoses of the substance-type. Thus we must distinguish between sulphur, which we can hold in our hands as a piece of matter, and the sulphur-principle, which is hidden therein. Perhaps we could speak of archetypal sulphur (or primal sulfur). The term 'archetypal sulphur' points to a dynamic which is hidden in the substance, and which expresses itself both in the properties of sulphur in elemental form just as much in those of its compounds. The world of substance is comparable to a tapestry, woven using the substance types. (*Ibid.,* p. 305)

In order to get to grips with how Julius is using the term 'sulfur' it is helpful to consider the shift that is being proposed here. Sulphur is a substance. It can be experienced tangibly as a discreet sample in physical form. *Sulf* on the other hand, is a process which is by no means limited to the physical properties of sulphur. *Sulf* denotes a process whereby tangible, manifest forms dissipate, burn, de-materialize...characteristically with warmth and light arising in the process. We could take a completely different chemical element and denote it as *sulf* if its characteristic behavior or mode of interaction is that of expansion, dissipation, volatilization.

Let's explore this with a bit of imaginative 'element play.'

Oxygen, considered from the point of view of analytic chemistry, is an element with specific physical properties. These properties contribute to the way in which oxygen forms compounds and the way in which it interacts with other elements. These combinations and interactions are often described in terms of bonds and valences. This is one 'way of seeing' oxygen.

We could ask, in light of our present considerations, if oxygen—in its interactions with other elements—is *sulf* in its nature, or maybe its tendencies are *sal*, or perhaps it acts more as *mercur*.

Following on from the passage above, this question points toward the "dynamic which is hidden within the substance" rather than toward the static, quantifiable aspects of the substance. This question shifts our attention from the 'what' of oxygen to its 'how,' just as we did when we started to engage with dandelions as a being rather than a thing.

What emerges from engaging with oxygen from the dynamic perspective of the Tria Principia is the following insight: it depends on the context!

In combination with carbon, oxygen contributes a *sulf* tendency and aids in the volatilization of carbon to create 'heavy air'—carbon dioxide. Oxygen, in this instance, contributes to the freeing up of carbon from its tendency to form structures, scaffolds, rigid forms. With the help of oxygen's *sulf* activity, we are able to constantly liberate the carbon from our bodies which would otherwise lignify us into rigid people-pillars.

In its dance with hydrogen, oxygen takes on a very different role and reveals—in the remarkable fluid *water*—a *sal* tendency. Hydrogen is the lightest element—highly combustible and prone to dissipation. This ephemeral, volatile element 'comes down to earth' in combination with oxygen, a great mystery of mysteries.

Oxygen can, furthermore, be found to be an intermediary between the extremes of carbon and hydrogen (*sal* and *sulf* in elemental forms) in the carbohydrates. Here oxygen takes on the role of *mercur*, mediating the structural, form-giving tendencies of carbon and the dissipating, volatilizing tendencies of hydrogen. It seems that oxygen can—in its interactions with other elements—be either *sal, sulf,* or *mercur,* and herein lies one aspect of what is revealed through an imaginative, alchemical way of seeing.

Considering the dynamics of each element in this way we come, as indicated by Rudolf Hauschka, to the possibility of understanding substances (such as carbohydrates) as the manifestation of the different qualitative *activities* of their constituent elements. Cellulose reveals a dominance of the *sal* tendencies of carbon, sugars (such as glucose) reveal a dominance of the *sulf* nature of hydrogen. Hydrogen's *sulf* nature comes even more to the fore in the essential oils and hydrocarbons—extremely volatile substances.[52]

The realm that is revealed through taking hold of the elements of chemistry imaginatively and through a consideration of *sal, sulf,* and *mercur* is the *dynamics* of substance, not 'things,' but activities. Julius emphasizes that his engagement with the Tria Principia in chemistry arises from the view that the chemical elements which have received so much attention for the last centuries are not primary building blocks out of whose combinations life *arises* but—quite the opposite—are endpoints in the disassociation of life, of living processes. He writes, "it is not possible to explain the processes in living organisms out of an interaction with matter. But, we can very well trace back the characteristics of the substances to their specific connections with life. Life is primary: our view of nature must be life-centered" (*Ibid.*, p.15). It is significant that a chemist seeking to re-enliven his science, and to make it relevant to the realms of life, has placed at the outset of his articulation of a positive direction for chemistry the three Philosophical Principles of the alchemists!

Mineral Matrix

From the end stages of ultimate differentiation and splitting, the path leads back to an original threefoldness of quartz, feldspar and mica-hornblende, which means to rocks from which threefoldness begins, rocks in which threefoldness is subordinate to the force of one uniform, superior essence.

— F. Benesch, *Silica, Calcium and Clay*

---

52. See *The Nature of Substance* by Rudolf Hauschka for more considerations such as these.

A natural progression suggests itself from chemistry to geology. Here we are confronted with a realm that seems to lend itself to a straight-forward analysis—or solve—and to reveal its secrets in the analysis of its parts. It could be said that the whole realm of geology exemplifies *sal* on a grand scale, the result of forming, condensing, crystallizing substances and that there is little *mercur* or *sulf* to speak of in this ossified realm (certainly little 'spirit' or 'soul'). This depends, of course, on our way of seeing!

In the introduction to *Silica, Calcium and Clay*,[53] Dr. Ross Rentea. presents the following description of the way in which a renewed *imaginative* grasp of the Tria Principia can inform an in-depth study of the role of silica, calcium and clay in the mineral, plant, animal, and human realms, describing them as "gates to all further understanding of natura" (1995, p. x). He continues:

> On a … spiritual level these three substances (silica, calcium and clay) perform activities known throughout the Middle Ages as the principles of sal, mercury (or mercurial), and sulfur. During the Middle Ages these three principles were considered profound activities rather than substances. The sal quality was seen wherever earth-like substances connected with a watery substance; the mercurial wherever the watery, fluid elements connected with the airy (where, for instance, foamy substances appear in the more crystallic world or the creation of leaves appears in the plant world); and the sulphuric as the connection between the airy and the fiery.

What is made clear throughout the book, and where an initial reference to the Tria Principia is significant, is that the authors are not referring to silica, calcium, and clay in a solely material sense but show that these substance-activities are present in a wide range of natural processes. In order to make this distinction clearer the authors adopt the terms *silicic, calcic, and clayish* when the process is the focus, and silica, calcium and clay when the more familiar mineral substances are being considered.

---

53. By Dr. Friedrich Benesch and Dr. Klaus Wilde, published by Schaumburg Publications.

From the outset of these geological considerations we can imagine that the silicic rocks have their genesis in the fiery, *sulf* processes connected with intense heat and dramatic forces, such as those of volcanism. The *calcic* rocks have their origins in the totally contrasting conditions of the watery realms, the gradual precipitation into layers of sediment with clear planar stratification—*sal*. In between these two, the *clayish* rocks arise out of metamorphosis brought about through the rhythmical or radical interplay of warming and cooling, wetting and drying, pressure and release.

An alchemical world view does not undertake a study of natural phenomena by isolating the phenomena being studied from its context. From this perspective, the way in which substances show up in the 'earth body' can find resonances in other 'bodies.' In the life processes of plant, animal, and human the *calcic, clayish,* and *silicic* are revealed in ways which elaborate upon and reveal the qualitative dynamics hidden within their material 'endpoints' in the rocks of the earth. I will once again share an imaginative approach to engaging the Tria Principia in considerations of the mineral realm through a brief consideration of two contrasting landscapes. This approach (following on from Wilde, Bockemuhl, Bosse and others) arises from my own biographical engagement with locations informed deeply by the *silicic* qualities of the granitic Canadian Shield (on the one hand) and the *calcic* qualities of the Cotswolds in the UK. The former was a deeply formative landscape in my youth, the latter has been my place of dwelling for well over a decade.

Canadian Shield

The Canadian Shield is a sizeable area of exposed igneous and metamorphic rocks in central, eastern, and northern Canada. Much of the Shield bedrock lies at or close to the surface and the ancient, volcanic-born rock is now weathered and worn after tens-of-thousands of years of seasonal fluctuation, glaciation, and erosion. My clearest impression of this area is of exposed granite boulders, speckled with mica and quartz faces glinting in the sun, wrapped with the gnarled roots of pine trees and lapped by the clear, transparent waters of innumerable lakes. Plants and trees make do with shallow rooting, or tap-root into granite fissures. During the heat of summer the air is filled with the aromatic scent of pine as the intensely volatile oils and resins vaporize into the atmosphere. The summer air is furthermore filled with the buzzing, biting, incessant swarming of a myriad of winged insects. Plants are conservative with their vegetative process, leaves toothed and lobed, flowers are small though often deeply scented. Blueberries ripen in the acidic soil and provide a treasured harvest of intense flavor and color. Wary white-tailed deer populate the woods with a nervous alertness, ready to bound away at an instant. Light shimmers intensely off rippling water and granite faces, penetrates deeply into the forest and the watery depths, and irradiates the earth. Throughout this landscape there is the impression of the dominance of *sulf* processes at work, and these —as dynamics arising out of the mineral matrix— echo the articulations of the *silicic* processes so clearly described by Wilde and Benesch. Needle-like leaves, intense aromas and flavors, winged carapaces and hyper-awakeness, a dominance of light.

Cotswolds

The Cotswolds, in sharp contrast to the Canadian Shield and its bedrock of igneous rock, is an area deeply informed by the Jurassic Limestone that appears only rarely in outcrops of rock and weathered cliff and is rather more visible in the raised up buildings, field walls, and steeples of its manmade creations. These buildings avail themselves of the raised up sea-bed limestone and its ease for shaping. In contrast to the wiry pine and fibrous ironwood of the Canadian Shield country, outside my window is a sea of green. Vegetation spills out over the ground, out of the woods, out of bush and out of field. My window-view is literally choked with leaves and dotted with bright flowers, many with an abundance of broad petals. I have never quite accustomed myself to the screen-less windows, for I have been deeply schooled in summers of biting flies and murderous mosquitoes. But here it is not so much the realms of light and air that are abuzz but more the 'underfoot' realms of a moist vegetation. Glistening trails of slime belie the many slugs and snails that forever munch through the undergrowth. In Canada we fence the vegetable patch against the deer, in my Cotswold garden it is a constant job to fend off the slithering masses from the tender plants that they seem intent on devouring. The garden plants that favor this limestone land are the brassicas and beets, the cucurbits and the peas. Though of course companions of human-kind, and not native to the place like the deer is to the Shield country, the dreamy cow and domestic sheep exemplify an aspect of the animal life that is at home in a landscape deeply informed by the *calcic* processes. "A picture for this entire process (the *calcic*) can be found in nature: a herd of cattle lying on a meadow in the moonlight chewing their cud. The totally motherly function of the calcic is active in chewing, breathing, digesting, producing milk, and eliminating."[54]

In summary

These brief explorations of the *silicic* and the *calcic* in terms of how they are dynamically active in the various living processes in contrasting landscapes touches on the way in which the Tria Principia can be brought to bear on the study of mineral matrices from an alchemical or dynamic perspective.[55] The two examples given above are of course indications only and landscapes are shaped and inhabited in particular ways due to a wide range of factors. It is significant, however, that a broad range of relationships is revealed on a variety of levels when the three processes of *sal, sulf,* and *mercur* are brought to bear in a consideration of the minerals.

The Human Being, The Plant, and the Mammal

These considerations of chemistry, minerals and landscapes are gradually drawing us toward a more focussed engagement with the biodynamic preparation and the questions that I have been pursuing throughout these pages. We are, however, still gathering.

The biodynamic preparations have taken hold of plant or mineral substances, animal organs, and specific conditions that touch on all

---

54. Benesch and Wilde, 1995.

55. For further study in particular reference to the Tria Principia in the mineral realm see Benesch and Wilde cited in the text or Dennis Klocek's *Sacred Agriculture: The Alchemy of Biodynamics.*

kingdoms of nature as well as on elements of time and place. The bio-dynamic preparation is not a product of a mechanistic process of design or creation but is one of a synergistic coalescence of dynamic activities. I am rooting this particular study of the preparations in plant alchemy because spagyrics reveals, theoretically and practically, the significance of the three philosophic principles through their manifestation in the plant world. As we are beginning to see, however, these three principles are at work (or play!) in more than just the plant world. They begin to reveal themselves as organizing principles throughout the myriad 'manifestations of matter' that science has occupied itself with so intensively. They are also, we will find, of significance for the human being. A study of the human being in light of the Tria Principia is very revealing, and will set the scene for a consideration of the mammal. This contribution is of course essential if we are to understand the contribution of animal organs to biodynamic preparations.

A Threefold Physiology

The anatomist Johannes W. Rohen is well known for his *Color Atlas of Anatomy*, a reference book used by medical students around the world. It is an example *par excellence* of an analytical study of the human body in order to facilitate the identification of the visible structures that make up the complexity of the physical body. However, in 2007, this world-renowned anatomist published a book of a different kind. In this book, *Functional Morphology: The Dynamic Wholeness of the Human Organism,* Rohen refers to the Tria Principia in the following passage:

> As early as the Middle Ages, the alchemists and Paracelsus (among others) were already aware of the significance of these three basic physiological systems, which they called Sal, Sulfur, and Mercury processes. They understood Sal as the tendency toward hardening, salt formation, and structural definition—the formative, informational element as it were. Sulfur was understood as chemical conversion, which is always linked to the transformation of matter and the release of energy. Sulfur encompassed not only actual

combustion but also the transformation of matter, metabolic processes as such. Mercury, quicksilver-like and mobile, constituted the middle, rhythmic element in this trinity, inserted between the polar opposites of Sal and Sulfur as a balancing and linking element. (2007, p.19)

Rohen's comprehensive study of human physiology takes these three processes as its basis and applies them in a *functional* study of the human being from the cellular level to the organization of the whole body. He provides the following illustration (redrawn from Rohen, p. 20) to illustrate this understanding of the basic functional processes of the human organism.

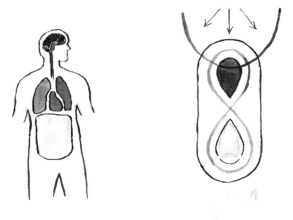

sal processes   mercur processes   sulfur processes

The functional threefoldness of the human body. The two polar functional systems—the information system (brain and sensory organs) and metabolic/ limb system (abdominal organs and extremities)—are connected, harmonized and balanced by the organs with rhythmic functions (respiratory system, cardiovascular system). (Ibid., p. 20)

Throughout his book Rohen uses the terminology he establishes in the caption above and table below (where I have added the terms *sal, mercur,* and *sulfur* for reference). The correspondence between the terminologies he uses and the Tria Principia is exact. Rohen furthermore makes a distinction between functional processes in the body (pictured above) and functional processes in the soul as informed by the Tria Principia. The following table illustrates the manner in which the processes are viewed in Rohen's study of the body and soul:

Information exchange	*Structural and informational processes*	*Nervous systam*	*Thinking (Sal)*
Rhythm, transport, balance	*Rhythmical processes*	*Circulatory system respiratory system*	*Feeling (Mercur)*
Metabolism	*Substance processes exchanges of matter and energy*	*Metabolic system*	*Willing (sulfur)*

Basic functional processes of the human body and their relationships to soul functions

As a physiologist, Rohen has found significance for the three processes in providing a study of the human organism in terms of its *life process* where anatomical and analytical studies lead to an understanding of its lifeless structure and mechanical actions. Rohen writes the following succinct passage about his sense of the contribution of a study based on *qualitative processes* to science and human understanding:

> If I have succeeded in engaging unbiased readers in a more 'living' way of thinking, perhaps I will also have contributed one small building block to the edifice of a new and accurately expanded science of the human being that will serve as a foundation not only for many specialized fields such as education and medicine but also for the development of human culture in general. (*Ibid.*, p. xvi)

Rohen is clear that the human being viewed in terms of the *functional threefoldness* of the *processes (Tria Principia)* underlying the human body and soul contributes to very practical fields of social life and their development. His conviction of its potential is made more evident in his most recent publication *Functional Threefoldness in the Human Organism and Human Society* (2011), wherein he proposes that many of the "flawed concepts" being applied in the economic realm, the political realm, and the social realm generally can be ameliorated through an understanding of the triad of functional principles detailed in his previous work.

These pointers toward the potential for the three principles to bear fruit in the consideration of the social realm go beyond this present study however. For the path being followed here is guided by questions of innovations in agriculture first and foremost. And though it may seem that a consideration of human physiology has little to do with the questions I have raised about compost preparations, a glance now at the realm of the *plants in relationship to the human being* opens yet another key insight into the synergies arising in the biodynamic preparations.

Inversely Related

How do the Three Principles *sal, sulf,* and *mercur* shed light on dynamics in the plant world? Through a study of the medicinal plant in light of the alchemical Tria Principia, significant relationships begin to emerge on the level of *functional processes* that are otherwise hidden through our tendency to place attention on the *object* of our attention rather than on its *dynamic.* This relationship, however, manifests in an initially surprising juxtaposition.

In Figure 6 the functional relationship of human being to plant is—at least in spatial orientation—reversed. Rohen's insights into the functional activities of *sal, sulf,* and *mercur* processes in the human corresponding to nerve processes, metabolic processes and rhythmic processes is one part of the puzzle. Ralph Twentyman in his book *The Science and Art of Healing* (1992) describes the corresponding processes in the plant in a consideration of the medicinal action of the lilies:

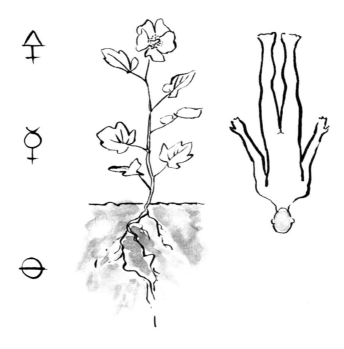

The functional relationship between the three Principles in the human being and the plant.

In the old alchemical tradition the root process was called Sal or salt and the blossom process Sulphur, whilst the middle realm of stem and leaf was called Mercury...It is clear, using this way of looking at the living processes of nature, that in the lilies the Sulphur and Mercury processes predominate, the Salt processes are weak. The lilies have not come strongly to earth. We would anticipate that their chief actions within the human organization will be in the metabolic and genital realms, the sphere paramountly of the Sulphur processes, and in the rhythmic systems of the circulations and breathing which is the realm of the Mercury processes. And this is what we have found in the drug pictures. (Twentyman, 1992, p. 188)

Wilhelm Pelikan, author of *Healing Plants,* illustrates the relationship between human being and plant with reference to the functional relationship of the middle system—the rhythmic system.

The leaf takes carbon dioxide from the air. This goes through a process of carbon condensation and carbohydrate metamorphosis that essentially provides the material for the plant body. Oxygen is exhaled in the process. The human rhythmic system takes up oxygen in the chest organization and disassembles the 'carbon-ness' of the body, combating its dense nature and ejecting the carbon dioxide from it. Both processes proceed rhythmically between the fluid and airy spheres, but they go in opposite directions. (Pelikan, p. 2)

On the basis of these and many other examples of the functional relationships between processes in the plant and their corresponding "polar opposite" activity in the human, Pelikan gives a very cogent basis for understanding the medicinal properties of plants which does not rely solely on the analysis of chemical actions and isolated mechanisms. The whole human being, and the whole plant, are kept in mind throughout—the one informing the other.

Plant life also has contrasting elements of dissolution and hardening, the latter in its root functions, the former in its flowering processes. A rhythmic relation is established between them through the middle principle of leaf activity. However, in plants the dominance of either extreme does not lead to disease. Instead a creative principle produces variety of form.

Some plants are almost entirely root, with leaf and flower development reduced to a minimum. Others produce enormous flowers but hardly any root or leaf. (*Ibid.*, p. 11)

With insights such as these regarding the human being, on the one hand, and the plants' tendency to produce forms which exaggerate one or other of the plant organ processes, Pelikan establishes a "rational medical botany" with the diagram of correspondence above as its basis. It is in the realm of medicine—homeopathy in the case of Ralph Twentyman and herbal medicine in that of Wilhelm Pelikan—that a contribution of an understanding of the three principles to developments in science and human development is made evident once again.

Of Hooves, Horns and Antlers

The biologist Wolfgang Schad contributed a study of great significance to the life sciences when he published *Man and Mammal* in 1977.[56] Though perhaps still awaiting a wider recognition due to an ongoing investment in such ideas as random selection and the explanation of physical characteristics of animals based on narrow conceptions of 'survival,' Schad's book is situated squarely in a study of three-fold functional relationships. He takes as his departure point for a study of the mammals the three systems mentioned by Rohen—the nervous, respiratory or rhythmic, and the metabolic—though his work precedes Rohen's by several decades. Though not explicitly alluding to the processes of *sal, mercur,* and *sulfur,* Schad's study is exemplary of the potentials for the basic tri-unity of the three *processes* to inform subjects usually pursued with a more analytic approach. Schad attributes to Rudolf Steiner the insights he has into the three-fold human being as the basis for his study.

> (Steiner) proposed that the proper way to understand animal
> forms is by first comprehending the human form, for to his
> intuitive perception the nature of man showed itself to be a kind
> of compendium or summary, on a higher level, of the entire
> animal kingdom; and for him this truth came to expression in the
> harmonious, omni-potential form of man's body. So understood,
> man is the central and balanced configuration of which each
> mammalian animal species appears as a partial, one-sided
> development. (Schad, p.2)

Schad's study offers a very convincing and informative study of the mammals that sheds light on features of individual organisms as well as on various aspects of behavior, nutrition, life cycle and habitat. I will not go in to Schad's study at great length as I leave that to the interested reader to pursue further, however, I will briefly touch on the aspect of the threefold nature of the mammals through an illustration of three mammal types as

---

56. This is the first English edition, published by The Waldorf Press, New York. A new English edition is forthcoming from Adonis Press.

it will have specific bearing on the question of why certain animal organs were chosen for the creation of the biodynamic preparations.

Schad illustrates, through numerous examples, the dynamic threefoldness embodied by the different main mammal groups he identifies—the rodent, the carnivore, and the ungulate.

The squirrel is pictured below as a representative of the rodent group, the fox of the carnivore group, and the deer of the ungulate group.[57]

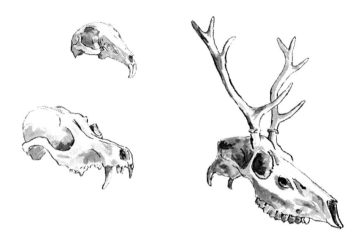

Where the three mammal groups manifest a dominance of either the nerve sense (nervous system/information processing/*sal*) in the rodents, rhythmic (rhythmic system/*mercur*) in the carnivores, or metabolic (*sulf*) systems in the ungulates, the human being (not pictured) has developed its organism on the basis of a functional harmony or balance between these systems.

Through a study of the *functional processes* and the tendency for each of the three mammal groups to be dominantly informed by one of these processes, new insights arise into their physiology, life cycle, behavior, diet, coloring—insights into 'parts' that are more often explained through

---

57. In *Man and Mammals* Schad chose to illustrate the cow, lion, and marmot as typical animals of the three types. The choice of animal types depicted here is based on representations of animals common to the author's place of residence and are illustrated from specimens from his collection.

an abstraction of their specific contribution to the animals' adaptive behavior rather than being seen as intrinsically related to the animal as a whole. This is yet another example of the potential for the Tria Principia to allow for *the making of distinctions without the loss of meaningful relation.*

Schad's book holds a wealth of insight and detail that can only be briefly touched upon, in this study. It is an invaluable contribution to illustrating the significance of the threefold, functional view of processes in 'making sense' of the mammals.

∞

One last example of how the Tria Principia is informing a renewal in the study of nature and the human being is worthy of note, particularly when considering the innovation of the biodynamic preparations.

This example concerns the question of the quality of *time*. This is a highly significant consideration for our modern world-view, which is largely unaccustomed to thinking in terms of the *qualitative influences* of time. Time has been quantified, mechanized, and homogenized in the great process of 'Enlightenment' rationalization. For the most part our relationship to time is purely functional—ordering our lives and actions in regular and predictable units.

Alchemically, however, time is anything but the 'tick-tock hours' of factory production. In the following example it is again the principles *sal, sulf* and *mercur* that provide a lens on a renewed *qualitative* relationship to time.

With this last example in mind it will then be possible to conclude this chapter with a discussion of the significance of all those perspectives explored in this chapter to the question of *understanding* the biodynamic preparations.

∞

Qualities of Time

In a study of the seasons of the year and the qualities that each season encapsulates, Rudolf Steiner presents the following picture. I quote it at length because in many respects it touches on several themes discussed previously.

If we now turn towards the inner part of the earth we come to the acid formation process and especially to the salt process, for the salts derive from the acids; and this is what the earth really wants to be. Hence when we look up into the cosmos we are really looking at the sulphur process. When we consider the tendency of the earth to form itself into a cosmic water drop we are really looking at the mercurial process. And if we turn our gaze to the solid earth underfoot, which in spring gives rise to all that we see as growing, sprouting life, we are looking at the salt process.

The salt process is all-important for springtime life and growth. For the roots of plants in forming themselves out of the seeds, depend for their whole growth on their relation to the salt formation of the soil. It is these salt formations—in the widest sense of the term—the deposit formations within the crust of the earth, which give substance to the roots and enable them to act as the earthly foundation of plant life. (Steiner, 1996, pp. 17-18)

In these passages Steiner considers the *sal, mercur,* and *sulf* processes in relation to the whole Earth and its environs. He also makes the very significant statement that the seasons and their qualitative influences can be understood through these processes as well:

Thus in turning back to the earth we encounter the salt process. This is what the earth makes of itself in the depths of winter, whereas in summer there is much more intermingling. For in summer the air is shot through with sulphurizing processes, which indeed occur also in lightning and thunder; they penetrate far down, so that the whole course of the season is sulphurized...during the summer too the salt process mingles with the atmosphere, for the growing plants carry the salts up through their leaves and blossoms right up into the seeds. Naturally we find the salt widely distributed in the plant. They etherealize themselves in the essential oils, and so on; they approach the sulphurizing process. The salts are carried up through the plants; they stream out and become part of the being of the atmosphere.

In high summer, accordingly, we have a mingling of the mercurial element, always present in the earth, with the sulphurizing and salt forming elements. If at this season we stand here on earth our head actually projects into a mixture of sulphur, mercury and salt; while the arrival of midwinter means that each of these three principles reverts to its own inner condition. The salts are drawn back into the inner part of the earth, and the tendency for the hydrosphere to assume a spherical shape reasserts itself—imaged in winter by the snow mantle that covers parts of the earth. The sulphur process withdraws, so that here is no particular occasion to observe it. In place of it something else comes to the fore during midwinter season. (*Ibid.*, p. 18)

Steiner here describes the processes in terms that are strongly analogous to those that we encountered in the spagyric process. There is a condition, Steiner indicates, where the three functional processes are more intermingled and 'mixed'—in and through the summer months—and a time of *solve* when they separate out into three distinct realms—in the winter months.

During this time (winter) the *sal* process is most influential in the earth "If therefore we observe the earth in the depths of winter, we have first the internal tendency to salt formation."

This indication that the three principles are active in the different regions of the Earth as well as in the seasons of the year brings us yet a step closer to understanding the Biodynamic preparations which—in light of all of the examples above—clearly arise out of a *dynamic and qualitative* understanding of substances and processes and not out of physico-chemical or mechanical relationships.

The *Bio* in Biodynamics

This alchemical journey following the path of the 'three-in-one' began with an observation: The Enviropig and preparation 505 (or what is often referred to as the Oak Bark prep) come into the agricultural domain through, it would appear, a synthetic thinking process that is attempting to create, out of this new synthesis, a beneficial solution to specific farming issues. Out of 'parts'—genetic information from mice, e.coli bacteria, skulls, oak bark—a new synthesis or 'whole' is created.

Although it was possible with the Enviropig to follow a causal connection between the parts and to see how they are being brought together in a mechanistic relationship through a verbal–intellectual mode of consciousness, this same type of cause and effect relationship was not so apparent in the Oak Bark prep. Research into spagyrics revealed a different type of thinking or way of seeing encompassed within the alchemical world view.

Although spagyrics undertakes an analysis or 'solve' of an original unity in order to obtain the products of that analysis (not unlike methods used in other sciences) the *leitmotif* of the Tria Principia maintains a meaningful relationship between the products of analysis so that mere fragmentation is not the result. Out of the initial plant body, 'parts' are obtained—essential oil, alcohol, and salt. A further reduction (to molecules, atoms, etc.) is not undertaken in the example of *spagyrics* and I would propose that the potential error in undertaking these further reductions is that greater distinction results although with an ever greater loss of meaningful relation.

The examples of the scientists encountered in this chapter, who are once again taking up the perspective of the Tria Principia, offer a way of seeing (rocks, plants, chemical elements) that restores meaningful relations to phenomena that had otherwise suffered the great reduction and had become the products of chance, accident, or random variation.

It now becomes possible to see how a holistic, exact imaginative mode of consciousness informed the combination of parts chosen in the creation of the Biodynamic preparation. The 'parts' of the Oak Bark preparation begin to reveal a synergy in their *dynamic* or alchemical properties as seen from the perspective of the Tria Principia.

Oak Bark Preparation: Synergies

Oak Bark is the product of the deposition (*sal*) process in the life activity of the growing tree. It is an exudation from that region of the tree most under the influence of mineralizing, hardening processes. The trunk of the tree is *raised up Earth*.[58] The bark is the deposition, hardening, crust-like formation that precipitates out of the thin layer of life that surrounds this mounded earth, the cambium of the tree trunk.

Oak bark is also very high in calcium (Steiner, 1993, p. 101). Calcium and the *calcic* are related to *sal* in the tri-unity of silica, calcium, and clay (Benesch and Wilde). The skull, and in particular the brain case wherein oak bark is placed, is the region of the body most closely associated with *sal* processes (Rohen) as it is where the nerve-sense system and its organs are most concentrated in their activity.

Considering the skull and its cranial cavity leads to the awareness that, within the whole organism, it is in the brain case where a certain 'stillness' or immobility arises due to the enclosing 'cave' of bone and suspension in the cerebrospinal fluid. This stillness provides the conditions for *sal* processes—in the animal these are processes of consciousness—to take place.

This process is taken to a particular height of expression in the human physiology wherein processes of consciousness and reflective self-awareness reach a significant level of development in the relative stillness of the cranium and its concentration of sense organs and nerve tissue (Rohen). Life processes, metabolism, rampant growth are all radically suppressed in the cranial cavity wherein organs are housed that are then more able to engage with the realm of thoughts and creative ideas intuited from outside the organism. This picture is, on another level, relevant to the mammal as well as to the human, although processes of consciousness and particularly self-consciousness, do not develop for the animal to the extent that they do for humans.

---

58. "If we look (at the tree) with understanding, the only parts that we can consider plant-like are the thin green stems, which bear leaves, flowers, and fruits. These shoots grow out of the tree in the same way as herbaceous plants grow out of the soil. As far as what is growing on its branches is concerned, the tree *is the* soil. It is mounded up soil, soil that is simply in a more living condition than the soil in which our herbaceous plants and grains are growing." (Steiner, 1993, p.139)

The winter months are the time in which the *sal* processes are dominant in the life cycles of nature (Steiner). What emerges from a consideration of the Oak Bark preparation in light of the *Tria Principia* is that it is based on synergies, a bringing together of substances or rather *functional processes* from the mineral (calcium/lime), plant (oak bark), animal (skull), and the seasonal qualities of time (winter) in order to enhance this *process or principle—sal* or the *calcic—*in the organic realm.

A step has been taken. Synergies and analogous relationships begin to become apparent.

We have arrived at a significant threshold, but before we break out the bubbly a cautionary note needs to be sounded.

Considerations of the Three Philosophical principles reveals that a design process lies behind the Oak Bark preparation that is not random or non-sensical. Rather, what becomes apparent is that a different kind or way of seeing and knowing lies behind the creation of this, and other preparations. This different way of seeing/knowing arises as a fundamental element of biodynamics, which reveals itself as not merely a new approach to work on the land, but as an impulse arising from the cultivation of consciousness through an exact imaginative consideration of dynamic processes informing the becoming of mineral, plant, animal, and human.

Sal, sulf, and *mercur* processes, considered as we have done in this chapter, point toward a dynamic realm which reveal relationships and correspondences otherwise lost to a purely analytical and classification approach to the natural world.

There is a danger, however, with the process as described thus far—in alchemy and in consciousness. That danger is what I call *the turning point.* It is a poignant point which holds within it the essence of questions that have been posed since the outset of this book regarding the polar dynamic of *right separation* and *right synthesis.* Navigating this turning point is the heart of the matter, and is even now all too easily overstepped.

This crucial point in this journey into biodynamics and alchemy will be the focus for the next chapter.

8

The Turning point

"Tragedies happen; people get hurt or die; ..."

Ok, I admit it. I do like to talk about spagyrics and the alchemical worldview, it's even been something of a theme for me these last few years. Ask me about it and I am sure to delve in happily and discuss the joys and challenges inherent in the processes of solve et coagula.

...And so, on a day in February, as days begin to lengthen, I find myself once again taking colleagues—whose curiosity and interest has been sparked by my animated descriptions of plant alchemy—into the workshop to describe the process, to show them the wondrous 'body,' 'soul' and 'spirit' of mint in their little bottles.

We go through the whole process—the distillation of essential oils, the pressure cooker, condenser...the making of wine wherein the plant 'gives up the ghost.'... the rectification of spirits, the incineration of plants in the 'dragon.'...the many attempts to get good crystals....the whole process of solve.

Separation and purification.

I then describe the next step...bringing the three back together again in the process of coagula.

From the point of view of the practical process, this means that the salts are placed in a flask, the essential oil poured over the salts and left to 'imbibe,' the spirit is added to these two and the flask set so that the three substances can—over time—'re-marry' in the flask.

And then the question.

It comes again... not for the first time...we have been here before...

Having described the whole process in some detail, right up to the re-combination of the three principles in the flask—the question comes again...

"I still don't understand the coagula stage. What is the coagula stage?"

A bit of frustration rises, slight irritation, what...is it the way I am describing it? Not describing it? What don't you understand...??

Followed by a realization....yes, hmmm, this is a good point...what really is the stage of coagula?

It seems, from a purely practical point of view, the most straightforward of the whole lot.

All that is needed is one vessel.

The three substances are added, kept warm, and...hey presto!... a new 'compound' is produced!

It seems—in the simplest of terms—a matter of mixing stuff back together again.

But why is that such a GOOD question?

I realize that here I am given a gift from my colleague.

Getting to grips with this stage of the process is THE key question with regards to 'right synthesis.' In it hangs the difference between funky-pigs and preparations.

This, at least, is my hunch—which I soon set to following up....

∞

Just as a thorough consideration of *right separation* or *solve* revealed a functional threefoldness informing a wide range of processes in mineral, plant, animal and human, it is now necessary to delve deeper into the complementary process of *coagula*, or *right synthesis*.

As a step toward getting to grips with the significance, poignancy even, of the stage of *coagula* (alchemically) or right synthesis (more broadly), let me return to the practical example and leitmotif of an alchemical perspective. How is the stage of *coagula* undertaken in plant alchemy?

The three principles *sal* (body – salts), *mercur* (spirit – alcohol) and *sulf* (soul – essential oil), having been separated and purified, are prepared in the following way: The salts are ground, placed in a flask and the essential oil poured over the salts and allowed to "imbibe until saturation." After a few days, the alcohol is then added and the flask is corked and a circulation established. This process is classically undertaken in a specially designed vessel called a 'pelican.'

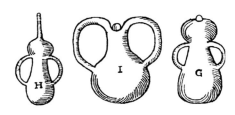

A *circulation* is brought about through the warming of the lower chamber of the flask (traditionally by being placed in a pile of decomposing horse manure). The liquids in the flask begin to evaporate and rise through the narrow neck into the top chamber.

The vapors expand in the top section of the flask and, through cooling, condense on the inside walls of the upper chamber and then run down the 'arms' into the bottom chamber of the flask again. Through this circulation—undertaken over time—the three principles are re-united into what alchemists call a *Clyssus.*

The Clyssus is a preparation of recombined extracts of one plant. In his *Magiae naturalis libri viginti*, Johannes Baptista Porta says, *"The Clyssus is the extraction of the subtlety of all parts of the plant, which flows together into a common being."*

Now, digging a bit deeper into theory and practice, it is in many ways not accurate enough to have described the process only in the way I have done above. Not, at least, if we are to follow an alchemical methodology. For what has been described is only the technical or practical process 'locally' in the lab (or dung heap!).

It becomes apparent, the more one studies and works with this latter stage of the spagyric process, that there is much more to this synthesizing process or 'alchemical marriage' than a mere mixing or recombination of parts derived from the initial stages of the Work.

Allusions to the three principles "flowing together into a common being" through a *circulation* suggest the arising of a *new organism*, not just a new amalgam of parts. Junius writes of this process, "circulation is an improvement of liquid substances" (2007, p.164). Alchemists refer to the process as an "Exaltation." Paracelsus says that one part of a medicine "exalted" in this manner "has the same effect as the two-hundredthfold quantity of corresponding dry plants."[59] The key term that encapsulates the whole intention of the process is, I feel, the *exaltation* of the three principles, whereby they are re-combined or re-synthesized but

---

59. "Until today science has been unable to explain why circulation, especially rhythmic circulation, causes an exaltation of the product. It is similar with homeopathic potencies. Experience proves their validity again and again, but an explanation is beyond the present state of official science." (Junius, p. 157)

to 'new heights,' into a "common being." Through a rhythmic process (repeated circulation—*mercur*) <u>in time</u>, a movement between the polarities of condensation or consolidation (*sal*) and evaporation or dissipation (*sulf*) unfolds, imbuing the medicine with attributes that go far beyond the purely chemical properties of the substances themselves.

Considering the process of *coagula* more closely, it becomes apparent that it asks for a reversal of several of the conditions which were necessary for the initial *solve*—or separation. These are not only or merely those conditions related to the more 'outward' work in the laboratory (types of heat, types of vessel) but also—and perhaps more significantly—processes that are more 'inwardly' located in the soul life of the alchemist. The alchemist must change his or her own approach *in consciousness* if the alchemical process is to unfold aright—as a mutually unfolding 'inner' and 'outer' process, each mirrored in the other. In order to make this key point more explicit, let us briefly revisit the type of consciousness that is applied in undertaking a process of *solve*.

Right Separation

Rudolf Steiner highlights the *solve* activity or function in consciousness as being that of the intellect. He writes in his book *A Theory of Knowledge Implicit in Goethe's World Conception*:

> Making distinctions…is the task of the intellect (*Verstandes*). It has only to separate concepts and maintain them in this separation. This is a necessary preliminary stage of any higher scientific work. Above all, in fact, we need firmly established, clearly delineated concepts before we can seek their harmony. But we must not remain in this separation. For the intellect, things are separated that humanity has an essential need to see in a harmonious unity. Remaining separate for the intellect are: cause and effect, mechanism and organism, freedom and necessity, idea and reality, spirit and nature, and so on. All these distinctions are introduced by the intellect. (Steiner, 1996)

Steiner goes further and really sums up the conundrum faced by the mind at the point where a clear distinction, classification or separation (solve) has been achieved when he states very succinctly "the intellect itself is in no position to go beyond this separation. It holds firmly to the separated parts."

From an alchemical perspective, this activity of the intellect gives rise to the clarity and distinctness of those elements analyzed out of their previously 'given' state—clear and distinct but nonetheless *corpse-like* in their nature.[60]

Whether we consider the concepts arising from an intellectual process in consciousness or the products separated out from a being or process in nature through an analytical procedure in the laboratory, the products of the process of *solve* are seen—alchemically—as 'corpses.'[61]

Let's be clear, in light of the spagyric process that has informed these considerations throughout, that *separation*—the deriving of clearly distinct and discrete products obtained through analytical processes—is *the* aim and objective of all of the laborious work undertaken up to a certain point. I am highlighting the importance of this in terms of *right separation* as this must be done thoroughly and rigorously.

However...

It is essential to recognize the turning point– the need to shift—if the activities essential for the process of *solve* (the intellect, destructive fire, analysis) are not carried over unchanged when the stage of *coagula* is approached. "If the (intellectual view) is regarded as an end in itself

---

60. We must disregard carbon in the broken-down form in which we know it when it has gone through various natural processes and emerged as anthracite or graphite. Instead, we must look at it in its activity in the realm of the living, as it passes through the human or animal bodies or builds up plant structures as only it can do. Then we realize that the amorphous stuff we imagined carbon to be is only the last remnant, the corpse, of what carbon actually is in nature's household. (Steiner, 1993, p.46)

61.Various authors allude to this way of referring to the products of living processes. Hauschka writes:"When we describe carbohydrates as the product of interacting carbon, pyrogen, and biogen, we are not speaking of an atomistic combination of these three substances, but rather of an interweaving of cosmic qualities which produce a unified substance, starch, in its various metamorphoses. It is only when this organic unit is destroyed that the three substances fall away like 'corpses' from the living organism." And further,"It will become evident later on that all the chemical elements known to science at the present time are more of less in the category of waste products—corpses—of organic life." (Hauschka, pp. 43; 24)

instead of as a necessary intermediary stage, then it does not yield reality but rather a distorted image of it" (Steiner, 1996).[62]

This reference to the 'corpses' of either living processes in nature or of consciousness relates directly to considerations I have raised in the realm of biodynamics, as can be seen from the following:

> The motion from the Being to the manifestation is what very often causes confusion in biodynamics with regard to substances. Because substances are the manifestation of a condition of Beingness. They are not in themselves Beings, but substances are the corpses of beings. There is a polarity there, between what has manifest as a substance and what is potential (*in potentia*) in the cosmos, as a Being, which is going to make an appearance. And that potential Steiner has characterized in many places as the difference between the process and the substance. The process is equivalent to the Being. It is the non-manifest. It is a silica process that is not silicic acid, silicon, any of those. It is an archetypal, supersensible, cosmic potential for silica, silicon, silicates, to actually manifest. It is useful to us, very important when we begin to see these differences between something as a substance and something as a process. (Klocek, 2013.)

So how are we to understand *coagula*—what are the appropriate conditions for right synthesis?

Right Synthesis

The process of spagyrics is our touchstone, let us return to it for its clarity of practical illustration.

'Outwardly,' the process of re-uniting the salts, oil and alcohol into a 'common being' is undertaken in a vessel called a pelican. But we might ask—why a *pelican*? It seems an odd way of describing a vessel, such as the one pictured below from a museum in Poland, that looks more like a human torso than a bird…

Once again we find direction in the imaginative consciousness of the alchemical worldview.

The alchemists used various different images to depict the whole process of transformation and, as this has previously been noted with regards to heat or 'warmth,' images are often chosen for the multiple meanings they contain. Birds are one example of a type of image that is used to depict a transformative process which unfolds in stages or as a series.

The image of the pelican (fourth from the left) is depicted in the sequence reproduced above. As in our previous encounter with a 'hen,' where we found that that image spoke to a type of warmth (which would ultimately suggest a type of apparatus or vessel, such as an incubator), an inner attitude of the operator (patience!) and a quality of time (different operations—organisms—have specific incubation times before they 'hatch' or mature), so will we also find multiple layers of meaning with further consideration of the image of the pelican.

Dennis Klocek[63] writes of the pelican;

The bird symbol in the Sun stage is the Pelican.[64] *In olden times it was thought that the pelican tore at its own breast in order to feed its young with blood. This symbol of self-sacrifice is found on altars and vestments in many churches. Biologically, the pelican actually tears out the down on its breast, and the exposed flesh becomes filled with blood vessels so that the bird can keep its eggs warm during brood rearing. Whatever the case, the image is one of* give-away, *of self-sacrifice.*

To contextualize this stage of the pelican in the present discussion, this crucial stage (*coagula*) is one that depends on an attitude of self-sacrifice on behalf of the alchemist (or scientist) so that the 'marriage' or 'exaltation' can take place as a touching in — grace — from the living and unifying realm of the spirit. The pelican (vessel, image, process) reminds the alchemist that in order to obtain a *right synthesis* he/she can only work to create the right conditions for this marriage — they cannot force it or manipulate it.[65]

The alchemist must be diligent and directed in the preparation of the entities that will later be synthesized anew, readying them for 're-marrying' into a new synthesis. This has been described at length in terms of *solve* — separation and purification. It is an active process, directed by the alchemists' intent through mind and hand... 'my will be done.' Once the initial stages have been achieved and a re-synthesis of the separated elements is approached, the alchemist must navigate the turning point (imaged as the pelican) and undertake a change or reversal of the will. This is a shift, a process of give-away... 'thy will be done.'

The poignancy of the turning point lies in the fact that without navigating this stage in the process, either the faculty of separation continues beyond a crucial point and leads to greater and greater fragmentation or a false synthesis arises, a 'false reality.'

---

63. Klocek, 1998.

64. The stages in the alchemical work in planetary terms will be elaborated on further in Chapter 9.

65. This aspect of the alchemical worldview has been discussed in the context of Heinrich Khunrath's emblem *amphitheatrum sapientae aeternae* in Chapter 4.

Summary and correspondence

Separating and co-ordinating are two inseparable acts of life. Perhaps it is better to say that, whether we wish it or not, it is unavoidable for us to proceed from the whole to the parts and from the parts to the whole. And the more vitally these two functions of the mind are conjoined, like breathing in and out, the better it will be for science and its friends.

— J.W. Goethe

From the perspective of the spagyric process, the movement of substances between the two chambers of the pelican creates a rhythmical circulation between two polar regions or conditions that foster the process of *coagula*. In the transition between the fluid state in the lower chamber (fluid = ponderable) and the vaporous state (imponderable) in the upper chamber a 'new being' arises. From an alchemical perspective the *ponderable* state of substances gives them a relation to the earthly, manifest realm of observable nature and the *imponderable* state gives them a relation— 'opens' them—to the influences of the cosmos (stars, planets, qualities of time).

This alternation between dissipation and condensation has many analogies when considered from the more 'inwardly' oriented perspective. It is analogous, in its movement between the ponderable state (liquid) and the imponderable state (vapor), to the experience in human consciousness of the movement between being 'embodied'—awake—and 'dis-embodied' or ex-carnated—asleep. It is the movement between the conscious pole, where we have awareness of the products of consciousness (and gain self-consciousness), and the superconscious pole, where we are 'open' to the imaginal, but unconscious, having given-away our consciousness of self.

The alchemical vessel for consciousness is our *own attention,* and the substances in the vessel are the sense impressions, images, questions, feelings, remembered snippets of conversation, etc. that come to us in the process of the Work. The circulation is the active pondering, imaginative contemplation, which 'circulates' the impressions through an active attention that is, at the same time, 'open,' receptive, listening. As the images and questions are warmed through the attention, by paying attention, they are opened, and made receptive to the meaning encoded in the imaginal nature of what is being contemplated. Insight, a meaningful coalescence of previously discreet elements in the 'vessel' arises in a flash or flowering of insight. This is, after Kühlewind, a "touching into the superconscious;" or, after Bortoft, an experience of the "nonlinear, simultaneous, intuitive" nature of the holistic mode of consciousness.

The result of *this* type of process of synthetical understanding has many distinctive features.

- It cannot be forced.
- It arises from a *reversal* of the will—from 'my will be done' to 'thy will be done.'
- It arises 'in time' or over time, in its own time.[64]
- It may bring to light connections, correspondences, and relationships which *could not* have been determined by the intellectual mind and process which prepared the 'event' through *solve*.
- It is based on a gesture of 'opening out' rather than the 'narrowing down' characteristic of analysis and distinction striven for in the process of *solve*.

This reversal of the will is, I propose, the key difference between *right separation* and *right synthesis*.

Biodynamics ~ Science or Art? Ritual or Magic?

At the beginning of this book I posed the questions: *Can biodynamics be understood by the same scientific consciousness that has developed out of the study of the phenomena of the inanimate world? and Is biodynamics a science? A ritual? Magic?*

---

64. We find in all alchemical texts the admonition that we must first have an eye to the heavens before beginning all operations—either in the laboratory of practical works or in the laboratory of the mind. This eye to the heavens is not only to identify the particular influence of sun and moon and the qualitative influences understood to be generated by their spatial relationships (full moon, new moon, eclipse) but that the whole planetary realm, and indeed the zodiac behind it, was the source of *qualities of time* which were seen to have a marked effect on the resulting *Clyssus*. The significance of the *timing* of operations is deemed to be so important, in fact, that Paracelsus is known to have said (and I paraphrase) 'it doesn't matter what you do, it only matters *when* you do it.'

From an alchemical perspective, then, our first question when approaching the process of re-synthesis is: what is the time? This significance of the *timing* in the process of alchemy is further demonstrated by the fact that the process of *coagula* is undertaken through a circulation in the pelican for a specified period of time—forty days.

Science?

Having arrived at this point I would say that biodynamics, and the preparations in particular, are rooted in a rigorous science and study of substances and processes. This approach to science, however, engages and takes up both those phenomena that are 'outwardly' encountered—such as mineral, plant, animal, planet—as well as what arises from an 'inward,' imaginative contemplation of their dynamic nature. As I encountered through my meeting with Dandelion, the science of analysis and quantification contributes greatly to the *right separation* and identification of the physical nature of substances. As an end in itself, however, it provides only corpses.

If we wish to bring these corpses into meaningful relation, in order to once again serve as the basis for *life*, we must navigate the turning point. Undertaking science in this way amounts to a *metamorphosis of the scientist*[67] and not merely an expanded catalogue of knowledge arising from ever further analysis and finer separation.

Scientists such as those encountered in Chapter 6 are taking steps in the direction proposed in that they are re-engaging, in their own disciplines, with a way of knowing that reveals the qualitative, dynamic and *polarically related* relationships intrinsic within distinct categories of phenomena (Schad/mammals, Julius/chemical elements) *as well as* dynamic relationships between these categories themselves which are revealed as necessary distinctions only from the point of view of the analytical view of the verbal-intellectual mind.

For the verbal-intellectual mind there is no apparent relationship between the bark of the oak tree, the skull of a domestic animal, a period of time, an internment in a particular type of ground—let alone a sense for what the resulting substance may contribute to the compost heap. The intuition of their inherent synergies arises from a different way of seeing and a synthetical act that smacks more of an artistic approach than one of science. But hold on...wasn't art 'separated out' from science for good reasons? Isn't art going to taint the mix again with that suspicious ingredient—subjectivity?

---

67. This phrase, and an in depth exploration of its implications, is derived from Frederick Amrine's article "The Metamorphosis of the Scientist," in *Goethe's Way of Science.*

Art?

"Alchemists understand that, if they want to understand nature in a deeper way, it is necessary to work with consciousness so that what they call 'the artist' can harmonize one's consciousness with a specific level of consciousness found in nature." (Klocek, 2013, p. 23)

In the arts we find that a training for the type of process described above as 'coagula' is undertaken quite directly. It lies, in many respects, at the heart of the artistic process.

Let me give an example from my own experience.

In the many years that I spent on the stage as an actor, and in front of the stage as a director, I had the experience over and over again that in the arts—I speak specifically out of my experience in the performing arts—learning to navigate the turning point between 'my will' and 'thy will' was the much sought for, and rigorously prepared for, 'event' that resurrected the dead script into a living experience for actor and audience alike.

The preparation for performance is akin to the first stage of the al-chemical Work, where the play dies into the memory of the actor in the form of lines learned through repetition and rote learning, through the hours and hours of blocking scenes and technical refinement of de-tails. Right up to the time of performance, there seems to be an endless stream of details to remember, refine, define ...

The magic of the performance emerges however (though this cannot be controlled or determined), once an audience has gathered and the hours of preparation give way to the opportunity to *play* the play once again.

Over and over again I have encountered the moments when a shift occurs, when rather than 'acting' in the sense of 'I am speaking the lines I have learned previously and moving the moves rehearsed endlessly' there arises, for a brief period, the experience of being an instrument for the character to speak through me. It is an event that can only be prepared for, but not predetermined. It cannot be controlled or cap-tured and the Art of the actor is to get ever more skilled at creating the conditions for this emergence to arise. Once experienced—in a particular scene for instance—there is no guarantee that it will happen again in the same part of the play in the next performance. In fact, my experience is that it most often does not happen in the same scene, but in an entirely different one.

This event is also an event that unfolds and is informed by the particular location of the performance, the timing of the performance, the character of the audience members and their combined presence, the different progress of the performance (as in the notorious second night chaos) and the constellation of the actors.

Bringing an artistic discipline to bear in scientific enquiry is something which influential researchers of the past have alluded to in various guises. Natural philosophy, in its pre-Enlightenment form, has bequeathed us a wealth of examples of scientists whose skills in drawing, painting or writing were essential to the documentation and dissemination of their findings. This was, of course, in part due to these being the only means available at the time for recording physical features of their objects of study, but there is much more to this then mere historical limitation.

Goethe is known to have said

> He who possesses science and art,
> Possesses religion as well;
> He who possesses neither of these,
> Had better have religion.[68]

Biodynamics, in light of the above, in fact begins to reveal itself as a new synthesis of artistic consciousness and scientific consciousness, the beginning of a healing of that rift between heart and mind which was set in motion in the period following the demise of the alchemical worldview when they were more closely related, as Khunrath so clearly illustrated in his *amphitheatrum sapientae eaternae*.

---

68. *Wer Wissenschaft und Kunst besitzt,*
    Hat auch Religion;
    Wer jene beiden nicht besitzt,
    Der habe Religion
from *Goethes Werke* (1948, 1952), Vol. 1, 367. Cited in Max Jammer, *Einstein and Religion* (2002).

Muck and magic?

The path that I have followed to arrive at this point has been one that has delved deeply into the world of alchemy and spagyrics. A degree of detail has been explored due to the potential for the processes *solve et co-agula* to act as a touchstone for analogous processes in consciousness. I set out on this path by stepping off of an easily overlooked reference made by Rudolf Steiner in his Agriculture Course to an 'alchemy' which takes place in the natural realm if it is allowed or enabled to unfold according to its inherent laws.

There remains, perhaps, a question as to how justified such a return to alchemy is for seeking to shed light on contemporary agricultural practices. Or from another perspective, it will no doubt be said by some that if alchemy *is* a realm being turned to for an understanding of Bio-dynamics, surely this plonks this new approach to agriculture squarely in outmoded approaches to science, in methods which have long since lost their relevance.

The perspective that alchemy is pre-scientific and can have no relevance to our current age of technical and scientific wizardry—an age un-rivaled by any previous period of history—is deeply ingrained in most of us through our education and exposure to scientific rationalism.

Andrew J. Welburn, editor of Rudolf Steiner's *Alchemy: The Rise of the Mysteries* proposes, however, that:

> It is perhaps Rudolf Steiner's greatest contribution to the issue[69] that he can explain not only the spiritual truth that lay behind the inspired ideas of alchemy, leading up to a Newton and a Boyle, but how it is also a part of the whole development of our consciousness up to the present—*and into the future*. It is quite inadequate, from his point of view, to see alchemy as a past stage of science.

In the next chapter, this striking proposal that alchemy may have a *future role* in our search for knowledge will be taken up and explored further.

---

69. "The issue" being the relevance of alchemy in the modern world.

9

A Distillation of Words

"and you suffer and get old.
Nothing you do can stop time's unfolding ..."

Biodynamics was never narrowly focussed on agricultural techniques. It was conceived as a new way of thinking about farming, nutrition, and the world of nature…it offers a new holistic outlook that frees agriculture and science from the limits of a purely materialistic philosophy.

Richard Thornton Smith, *Cosmos, Earth and Nutrition*

I am at it again. Beakers and buckets, stills and receivers.

This time it is about water.

Out on the back patio behind the house there is a big Mexican clay oven, or chiminea. I have placed a broad, round tile on top of the chiminea to create a good level surface about four feet above the ground, out of range of the flotsam and jetsam of leaves and dust that the wind plays with at patio level. This round tile is the perfect place to put a large bowl for collecting rain water.

Bring on the rain, that 'heavenly dew!'

Now, don't get me wrong. I have had my schooling in chemistry. I carry around in my head (or thereabouts) that handy abstraction H_2O for the stuff that comes out of the tap or falls from the sky. Most of us do.

But it seems that for the alchemist there was a very different approach to this stuff than we have in our handy representation of a building block way of seeing.

And anyway, how can we make sense of the fact that two gases make up a liquid? How can two imponderables make a ponderable (speaking alchemically)?

How to grasp the revelation that a highly combustible gas is combined with the ultimate gaseous catalyst for combustion and we end up with something that puts fires out?

It was conundrums such as these that lead Goethe to look deeper into the phenomena of color, unsatisfied with the proposal that two (or more) darker 'lights' could combine to create white (colorless) light! I think chemistry could do with a bit of re-visiting.

Viewed from this side of the age of Enlightenment we have been led, via the great reduction of manifold substances to their chemical constituents and an ever increasing acceptance of quantitative ways of thinking, to accept a great homogenization of a previously richly differentiated experience.

Let me elaborate a bit.

Water is H_2O, right?...the stuff of life is a never-varying proportion between two chemical elements...

And even more radical, these elements are themselves—so we understand—made of quality-less protons and neutrons (or quarks, bosons, and what-have-you's) that are distinctly un-watery—once we get right down to the bottom of it.

Wherever we end up on that particular path of reduction (or solve!) we are led to believe that the stuff of the world is not the qualitative richness that Ronald Brady set out to engage with on his pursuit of a phenomenological chemistry, but is rather a distinctly quality-less realm accessible only to the mind of sophisticated mathematical reason and the wildly intricate technical apparatus of the one-eyed colorblind onlooker!

It has not always been thus.

Robert Allen Bartlett, a contemporary practitioner of alchemy, offers the picture that alchemists not only viewed water as qualitatively different depending on its source (dew, rainwater, spring water...) but that they also worked with water to obtain different fractions for use in specific operations or applications.

These fractions were all understood to have different qualitative nuances, obtainable through the solve of water itself.

This solve of water is undertaken by first distilling the chosen volume of water into four fractions—first to come off is the Fire of Water, next—the Air of Water and so on.

These four fractions are further distilled, each into three portions to give rise to the Sulfur of the Fire of Water, the Mercury of the Fire of Water, the Salt of the Fire of Water and so on until a full twelve fractions are obtained.

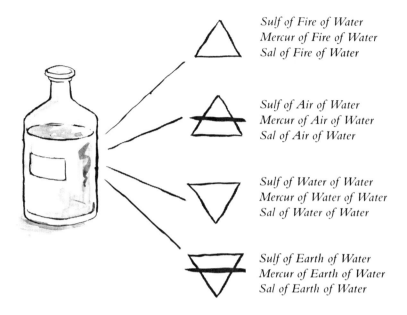

Sulf of Fire of Water
Mercur of Fire of Water
Sal of Fire of Water

Sulf of Air of Water
Mercur of Air of Water
Sal of Air of Water

Sulf of Water of Water
Mercur of Water of Water
Sal of Water of Water

Sulf of Earth of Water
Mercur of Earth of Water
Sal of Earth of Water

It would seem that for alchemists, water isn't just…well,…water.

All of this is of course a lot of wasted labor for anyone who is content to think of water as, at root, a bunch of particles of hydrogen and oxygen which (somehow) are in turn comprised of smaller particles, which seemingly differ (between one chemical element and another) only in arrangement, and not in kind.

For my part, there is enough in the suggestion that there are distinct qualities to water to suggest some interesting experiments with that wondrous liquid…

It's been a wet winter, and the cloudy incontinence has continued as spring begins to stir.

The large bowl I set out to capitalize on rainy events has now accumulated a good few liters of rain water.

I have also been up to one of the local springs and obtained some fresh, just-out-of-the-ground water. Time for some water play… it is now out with the stills, some receivers, and perhaps some radish seeds for sprouting trials.

Excuse me while I get back to the beakers…

∞

Could there really be a *future* for alchemy? Is that a real future, or merely a re-hashing of a relic of pre-scientific muck and magic?

Some significant challenges that arise when we consider a future for alchemy lie in the realm of *language*. These challenges are twofold (at least!).

On the one hand, the words/language that we have encountered so far; *solve et coagula, sal, sulf, mercur, Clyssus, exaltation...* have been used in this text to describe processes that have their origin in specific alchemical preparations (spagyrics) originating in the 16th century, and it therefore seems justifiable to use them primarily in the context of their original application. It could be argued, however, that just as our scientific method has changed, and our knowledge of nature become more precise, objective, and specific, a concurrent and necessary change in language has accompanied these developments. Alchemical terminology, from this perspective, quickly raises the ghosts of 'pre-scientific' mysticism and therefore *cannot* have contemporary relevance—it should be relegated to the historical archives of pre-Enlightenment science and left at that.

A second challenge arises when it becomes apparent that the terms *alchemy* and *alchemical* are (in spite of the above) reappearing in our everyday language, but now connected to anything from software to types of massage. These terms are being used in such a wide range of contexts as to become almost meaningless. It would seem, from this perspective, that there is nothing that limits the use of the term *alchemy* and that we are in a process of 'normalizing' something that at one time seemed esoteric and secretive though is in actual fact part of our everyday life as we embark on transformative healing or innovative design.

I tend to think differently.

Far from being either a quaint historical relic or a ubiquitous term for 'changing stuff,' I have found that in the alchemical worldview there is the potential to engage with words and with language in such a way as to open up new dimensions of mind. To do so, however, requires more attention to the nature of language generally, and then to the alchemical language in particular.

Disclosing, not just describing

Henri Bortoft writes that in order to understand the role of language in our scientific knowledge of the world (or even in our everyday experience) we must grasp the idea that language doesn't play a merely descriptive function in consciousness (a view that is easily held, consciously or otherwise) but that it plays a crucial role in *disclosing* reality:

> The origin of concepts is in the dawning of language, and we would never acquire concepts if language did not dawn in us. So the commonsense view that we see and know something *before we apply* words to it—which are therefore merely labels—clearly does not take into account the role of language in giving the concepts which enables us to see and know something *as* something in the first place. (1996, p. 311)

The *disclosive* role of language is so significant, and difficult to get to grips with (due to the nature of our language!) that I will defer further to Bortoft:

> Heidegger distinguishes between language as disclosure and language as representation—the former being primary, and the later being derivative and therefore secondary. He says that 'the essential being of language is Saying as Showing,' and that 'saying is in no way the linguistic expression added to the phenomena after they have appeared.' A sign is to be understood fundamentally as 'showing in the sense of bringing something to light.' (*Ibid.*)

Bortoft illustrates this role of language in 'disclosing' phenomena in an account of Helen Keller's personal experience of encountering water.[70]

---

70. In Helen Keller's experience, the word 'water' says water in the sense that it *shows* water (*not* points to it), whereby *water* appears. The word does not designate water *after* it has first appeared. But after it has appeared we take it that this is what the word does. This is the stage of dualism, when word and thing are separated and language becomes representational. Language as disclosure is saying-showing-seeing. This must be read holistically and not analytically, i.e., each of the three aspects is not a component part of the event of disclosure but the whole: saying *is* showing, and showing *is* seeing—like a threefold multi-perspectival figure. See "Understanding Goethe's Way of Science" in *The Wholeness of Nature*, p. 312.

It is one example of how words and language contribute to the appearance of the world.

The 'disclosive' nature of language has been recognized as being active in the learning of a language in childhood, particularly in the learning of the mother tongue. Wilhelm von Humbolt has referred to this process as the "energetic phase of language." Georg Kühlewind called it the "monistic phase."

Bortoft encapsulates a good deal of his extensive exploration of the disclosive nature of language in the following:

> Language is the medium of the *appearance* of 'the world.' There is therefore no 'world' outside language—and especially is there no world-in-itself hidden behind language which is forever inaccessible. (*Ibid.*)

For further insight into this highly significant articulation of the role of language in developing our *way of seeing* the interested reader can find a great deal more on this topic in Bortoft's book *The Wholeness of Nature.*[71]

To take up the thread of the alchemical worldview once more, it is now possible to explore what an alchemical language might reveal if we are to experience what *appearances* it affords.

There's water and then there's...Water

Let's take a word that has launched these latest considerations—water.

What comes to mind when you hear the word water? What images or ideas associate with this word?

Now, place this word in a particular context and again pay attention to what arises when you encounter it:

Earth, Water,[72] Air, Fire.

The scientific revolution, it could be proposed, began with water...with the demise of *Water* in the sense that this term had been used for a couple

---

71. See the section titled "The Twofold," p. 301.

72. Throughout the passages that follow the capitalized form (i.e. 'Water') will be used for when the Four Elements are referred to and the lower case (i.e. 'water') for the fluid that chemistry reveals to be a compound of hydrogen and oxygen.

of thousand years (at least) and the adoption of that same term to apply—to this day—to a very particular liquid understood primarily through the lens of analytical chemistry and used on a daily basis to brew our tea.

Let's recap briefly.

The fluid *water*—as a substance we encounter 'sensibly' in nature—seems to have a uniform composition. However, when subjected to the great 'solve' that was the hallmark of the rise of the science of chemistry, water revealed itself to be a 'compound' of two gases.[73] The new understanding of *water* that resulted from this act was one of many similar events which led to previously 'uniform' substances revealing themselves to be of compound nature. The fascinating story of the ingenious ways in which the chemical elements were teased out of their hiding places in the 'stuff of nature' is one of the truly remarkable events in the science of the last few hundred years. The result of this story is, however, that Water as it featured in the Theory of the Four Elements for the better part of two millennia, was relegated to the history books as an outmoded concept. This vague (it might be proposed) and indefinite concept was set right by the new 'enlightened' analytical science of chemistry.

This shift from Water to water—where the former was shelved in the archives and the latter adopted as the currency of science and school-book teaching—is, in my opinion, one of the most significant examples of throwing the proverbial baby out with the bathwater that has occurred in recent developments in consciousness.

Instead of maintaining a place for Water (alchemically) both as a dynamic condition as well as a way of seeing *while also* developing a science of water as a 'ponderable' fluid, the one was rejected in pursuit of the other. This radical rejection of the Theory of the Four Elements applied, of course, equally to the other Elements—and we were left to grapple with the much more homogeneous triad of solids, liquids, and gases.

I call this development a *homogenization* due to the fact that the Four Elements (Earth, Water, Air and Fire) can in no way be understood to be merely synonymous with the states of matter and the terms (solid, liquid, gas) which replaced them.

---

73. Revealed through the process of the electrolysis of water, attributed to Carlisle and Nicholson in 1800.

If we conceive of these states of matter in the manner in which they were taught to the vast majority of us in school science lessons, the primary difference between these states of matter is the spatial arrangement of the atoms and molecules of which they are made up. Ice, in this way of seeing, is made of the same constituent molecules as water, only these molecules are in 'close pack'—with little room to maneuver. Vapor, on the other hand, comprises the same molecules as water but with a much more expansive arrangement of molecules in space.

In terms of the molecular 'building blocks' of either ice, water, or vapor—we learn that these are all made up of the same chemical elements: oxygen and hydrogen.

The sub-story that accompanies this reduction (of ice, water, and vapor to arrangements of molecules) is one which ascribes a greater degree of accuracy and 'truth' to the atomistic view of substance than the previously held understanding of the Four Elements. This, at least, was my experience as a boy and young man being educated in the science of the day (20th century), and it is still a commonly held habit of reduction and homogenization. It focusses our attention in a uni-dimensional way on the most general aspect shared by solids, liquids, and gases—their elemental (chemical) make-up.

It's all Earth

Enter Rudolf Steiner. It is the early 20th century; a time when there were already a significant number of isolated chemical elements 'on the table' (72 at least). Mendeleev had already performed that great deed of classification and systematization leading to the periodic table... and, nevertheless, Steiner makes the remarkable proposal that:

> An ancient Greek...if he could appear in our present day world, would be prompted to say, "Well, this is all very well and good, these seventy-odd elements, but one does not get very far with them; they actually tell us nothing about the world. What you call your seventy-two elements all belong to what we call Earth; it is very nice that you differentiate it and analyze it further, but for us the properties that you recognize in your seventy-two elements

belong to the Earth. Of Water, Air, and Fire you understand nothing; of those you have no conception.[74]

And if this isn't enough to rattle the beakers, consider the statement made by Ernst Marti, a medical doctor well versed in the complex task of researching nature and the human being:

> When Rudolf Steiner gave the fundamentals for a new knowledge of nature through Anthroposophy, his first deed, which cannot be taken seriously enough, was re-founding the knowledge of the Four Elements. His works are permeated with ever new references to the nature of the Elements, their relationships, and evolution. (Marti, 1984)

What is Steiner playing at? Was he behind the times?
...or ahead of them?

Clearly there is more to Water, from the above indications, than can be neatly encapsulated in the knowledge that results from the 'solve' of its (or one of its!) manifestations as a substance in the natural world. Can the *word* Water, in its pre-Enlightenment sense, be re-encountered? What would such an encounter reveal? What does the alchemical term Water *show us*?

In order to approach this *word* and what it discloses, we must revisit the Theory of the Four Elements.

An Elemental Way of Seeing

For alchemists and those who continued to work with the Theory of Elements, an Element was not a discrete, physical or material entity but was rather a qualitative state or dynamic mode of manifestation—either in the world of nature or in the human body and soul.

The Four Elements are arranged in pairs in which Elements complement/oppose each other in their qualitative essences. In this way, Fire is characterized as being 'hot' and 'dry' whereas Water is 'cold' and 'moist.'

---

74. Rudolf Steiner, *Therapeutic Insights, Earthly and Cosmic Laws*, 1984, Mercury Press, pp.. 12–13.

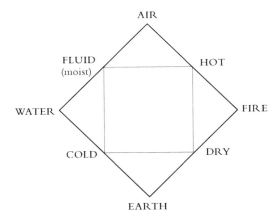

For our contemporary way of thinking the terms 'hot' and 'cold' are very quickly linked to the concept of 'temperature' as a quantitative measure—degrees Celsius, Fahrenheit, or Kelvin. This is an Earthly habit which has come to 'know' these qualities through their quantification in static degrees of heat. When we encounter these terms *alchemically*, we must hold back our habitual way of thinking. Our first task is to shift our way of thinking away from the reduction associated with thermometers and degrees—quantities[75]—into *dynamic qualities*.

From a *dynamic* perspective 'cold' can be imagined as a *movement*— and furthermore a contractive movement which tends to draw inward toward a common point. This can be illustrated as follows:

75. The innovations that led to the quantification of the *qualities* hot and cold, which gave rise to what we now know as a 'thermometer,' began in the 17th Century. Celsius and Fahrenheit were scientists of the 18th century, Kelvin of the 19th century.

This must be *actively imagined* as being a *dynamic* unfolding in three dimensions—it is not a static state, but an *active condition*. Even if something appears static, i.e. not moving (such as a chunk of granite), its state of 'coldness,' contractedness—as a *dynamic*—is not to be overlooked. Our tendency to think of it as being 'just there' is a habit which posits the granite as a 'thing,' an 'it,' passive and inert. But 'cold' is an activity, and from this perspective the granite is there for our attention to perceive only because it is very strongly under the influence of this qualitative dynamic.

'Hot,' on the other hand, can be imagined as an *expansive* movement (below), which expands in all directions outward away from a central point (or, to be more precise, expands *toward* the periphery in all directions).

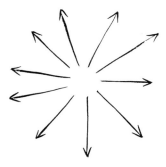

In short, 'hot' is an expansive dynamic, 'cold' a contractive dynamic. This is what, though constrained to a very narrow tube, the mercury in a thermometer is revealing[76] when subjected to fluctuations in 'temperature.' Furthermore, these *qualitative dynamics* were understood, in earlier times, as being observable not only in nature or in the manifest world *but also in the mind or soul of the observer*. Ernst Lehrs writes of this as follows:

> The terms 'cold' and 'warm' must be understood to have expressed certain qualitative experiences in which there was no separation

---

76. This is not at all a simple or straightforward set of phenomena to come to grips with. Ernst Lehrs devotes a chapter in his book *Man or Matter* to this subject, and Rudolf Steiner devoted an entire series of lectures (the *Warmth Course*) to an in-depth study of the nature of warmth.

between what is purely physical and what is purely spiritual. Expressions such as 'a cold heart,' 'a warm heart,' to 'show someone a cold shoulder,' etc. still witness to this way of experiencing the two polar qualities, cold and warm. Quite generally we can say that, wherever man experienced some process of contraction, whether physical or non-physical, he designated it by the term 'cold,' and where he experienced expansion, he called it 'warm.' In this sense he felt contractedness to be the predominant characteristic of Earth and Water, expansiveness of Air and Fire. (Lehrs, 1985, p. 182)

Depicted in a slightly different orientation, consider now the Four Elements in a different arrangement;

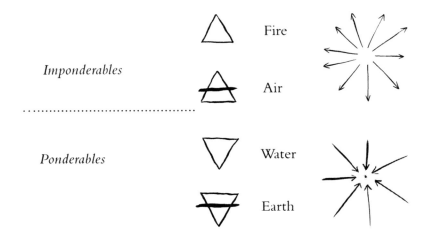

In order to better illustrate the *polarity* between the 'cold' elements Earth and Water, qualitatively expressing *contractedness* or—alchemically—a state of *ponderability,* and the 'hot' elements Air and Fire, the Elements are depicted above in a vertical orientation. The upper Elements, known to the alchemists as the *imponderables,* are understood to expand in all directions—*drawn to* the periphery—rather than being driven away from a central point.

The polarity that becomes evident through this orientation of the Elements is of central importance in the understanding of the contrasting nature of the 'upper' Elements and the 'lower' Elements.

Whereas for modern science, gravity is a primary force to reckon with in the world of matter, and movements perceived as moving *away from* a center of gravity are purely working against gravity to overcome it, a worldview that sees the unfolding of natural processes in terms of *dynamic polarities* understands the quality 'hot' as a dynamic in its own right. In modern language it has been suggested that *levity* is the best term to use to complement the otherwise singular force of *gravity* which alone is recognized by modern science.[77]

Through the observation of natural phenomena and inner contemplation of those observations, it is possible to deepen an experience of the *polar* nature of expansiveness/contractedness, 'hot'/'cold,' centripetal/centrifugal processes. In the instance of 'hotness' try and develop a sense for 'expansiveness' as being an active process which is related *to the periphery,* just as 'contractive' processes are related more to an 'inner' center. Lehrs sums this difficult, but important, dynamic up as follows:

> Considerations of this kind lead one to a picture in which the earth (planet) is seen to be surrounded and penetrated by a field of force which is in every respect the polar opposite of the earth's gravitational field. As the latter has its greatest intensity at its center, which is identical with the center of the earth's globe, so has the levitational field its greatest intensity at its circumference, which is somewhere in the width of the universe. As the gravity-field decreases in strength with increasing distance from the center of the field, that is, in the outward direction, so does the levity-field decrease in strength with increasing distance from the periphery, or in the inward direction. In both fields the direction of movement is from regions of lower to those of higher intensity.

It is very helpful to take the time to develop a good grasp of this deceptively straightforward relationship between two complementary (and fundamentally *polar*) dynamics. They are evident in a myriad of

---

77. The choice of illustrating this dynamic in its polar nature to that of the 'coldness' of Earth and Air arises from the work of Ernst Lehrs, George Adams, and Olive Whicher. For those who want to dive deeper into this incredibly significant work, further study of the publications *Man or Matter* (Lehrs) and *The Plant Between Sun and Earth* (Adams and Whicher) is recommended.

processes unfolding in the natural world and in the human being. This consideration of the qualities 'hot' and 'cold' is a primary example of a *polarity* which is grasped through *imaginative participation*.

Back to the question of what might be revealed in the language of the alchemical Elements...

Encountering *Earth*

It can be seen from the above that Earth is a manifestation or convergence of the qualities 'dry' and 'cold.' We could now take Steiner's statement to mind once more and consider what he might be referring to when he indicates that all the knowledge of a chemical nature that has been revealed in the periodic table is of an *Earthly* nature. The periodic table of the elements arises when 'matter' is disclosed *Earthily*, when we constitute our encounters with phenomena in a static ('dry') and abstract ('cold') manner. This *way of seeing* lends itself to the mathematics of quantification (atomic weight and number) and gives primacy to the part (the *abstract* in terms of something removed from its context) or—alchemically—the corpse.

In its 'dryness' and 'coldness,' Earth tends toward accumulating in forms that are self-centered. Surfaces present themselves to our sight or touch which relate to a common 'inward' center (what we would nowadays call the center of gravity of the object). These Earths have an integrity of surface which means that their orientation can be altered by external forces (such as our own will!) which may result in surfaces which were at first oriented downwards to be flipped to have a skyward orientation.

An Earth seems to have such a self-centered integrity and integrity of surface ('dryness') that it can be transported from one place to another revealing a kind of emancipation from context. This condition is most evidently revealed in the mineral kingdom, and quite succinctly so in the crystalline formations that arise in this realm. Pick up a lump of granite from Ontario and shift it to somewhere in England; the granite is not altered by this event; neither is the place of origin nor the new location.[78]

The Wateriness of *Water*

Alchemically, Water is 'cold' and 'moist.' It demonstrates the quality 'cold' in its tendency to fall, to accumulate in hollows or channels, and to gather together in drops, streams, ponds, lakes: It's moistness is evident in a tendency to be always in movement, flow, activity.

Where Earth is noun-like, Water is verb-like.

Water, in contrast to Earth, is not self-centered. The archetypal form of the fluid (or the 'cold' and 'moist) is the sphere. Whether this is revealed in the separating funnel during the distillation of essential oils from their host plant (Chapter 5) or in the great sphere of the watery planet on which we dwell, the integrity of surface for the Element Water is poised between an inner center and one which lies outside itself. The striking nature of the fluid condition is that this integrity of surface applies primarily to its uppermost surface, that which is oriented 'skyward.' Unlike the granite, it is not possible to change the orientation of this surface, to turn this face to be oriented earthward. Try as we might—in a closed bottle for instance—the fluid response to such alteration is to immediately re-establish itself with its 'ponderable' portion oriented earthwards, contained by the walls of whatever vessel it is in.

A further significant behavior of the fluid is that it always maintains one surface in a plane tangent to the center of the earth. To extend this

---

78. This at least seems to be the case for our usual way of seeing. It is arguable that both rock and place are changed, but this will not be taken up in the present discussion. There are, at least, few immediately apparent changes.

surface out horizontally in our imagination, and connect it with the surface of other 'bodies' of water in our environs is to realize that an (imaginative) unified surface of the fluid realm is a *spherical body*—a fluid sphere the size of our planet! Water is an Element of Planetary proportions—only seemingly separable into isolated portions, but in essence always 'listening' to a twofold call... the wish to unite into a planet-sized sphere and the tendency to give way to the expansiveness of peripheral dissipation.

Fluids respond—in great tidal rhythms and in flows of sap and blood—to the influence of bodies beyond our planet's surface. When we encounter the word *Water* and the *Watery* we should not therefore carry over a habit formed by Earthly thinking. We are invited, instead, to expand our attention to encompass both the local and the extra or supra-terrestrial—*simultaneously*. The fluid substance *water* plays such a crucial role in nature due precisely to this fact that it is poised between earth (Earth—ponderable, 'cold,' contractedness) and the cosmos (imponderable, 'hot,' expansiveness).[79] It is a 'go-between,' a catalyst— alchemically it is *Mercur*.

---

79. This dual nature of water (as fluid substance) is revealed through another intriguing lens. Rudolf Hauschka gives the intriguing proposal that correspondences between the alchemical Elements and the chemical elements can be explored once a qualitative way of seeing has re-established our understanding of what the alchemical language revealed. Hauschka proposes that the element Carbon (C) plays a significant role in the forming ('cold) and structural ('dry') processes in nature—and he links it with Earth. Oxygen's great role as catalyst for chemical change, its great abundance in the oceans of the world and its crucial place in processes of *life* gains it an association with Water. For the other Elements Hauschka explores the connection between Air and Nitrogen (N) and Fire and Hydrogen (H). What emerges from considerations such as these is a picture of water (fluid substance) that has a foot in two worlds...with oxygen situated in the realm of the ponderables (with carbon) and hydrogen placed in the realm of the imponderables (with nitrogen).

To consider Water as we have done above, on its own terms, as it were, is to encounter an alchemical Element that manifests in manifold dynamic expressions 'outwardly' in 'ponderable' nature. Engaging with this Elementary condition through imaginative participation has the potential, furthermore, to influence our way of seeing in such a way that we shift from an Earth mode of seeing or attention (which Bortoft has termed 'piecemeal') to a more dynamic mode of consciousness. This is a mode of consciousness that lives more in the verb-nature of words than in nouns—a concept that captured the imagination of poet William Stafford.

In The All-Verbs Navaho World[80]

"The Navaho world is made of verbs."

Left-alone grow-things wait, rustle-grass, click-
trunk, whisper-leaf. You go-people miss the hold-still
dawn, arch-over sky, the jump-everywhere glances.
This woman world, fall-into eyes, reaches out her
makes-tremble beauty, trolls with her body, her
move-everything walk. All-now, our breathe-always
life extends, extends. Change. Change your live-here,
tick-tock hours. Catch all the flit-flit birds,
eat the offer-food, ride over clop-clop land,
our great holds-us-up, wear-a-crown kingdom.

Here Stafford explores the way in which 'the world' *appears* if a language is structured in such a way as to emphasize the flow of experience—*verbs*. What arises is a highly dynamic encounter. All is movement, relational activity. Nothing static. Images are Protean, shape-shifting, and animate.

In Goethe's terms, Stafford engages with a world of *becomings*, not with an inert world of *things*.[81]

---

80. from *Even in Quite Places*, Confluence, 2010.
81. Consider the following: "Goethe counsels us to replace the concept of 'gestalt' or form, with that of 'formation' (or transformation), since "nowhere is there to be found anything at rest, finished." He further urges that, when we do use the word 'gestalt,' we should "certainly think of it only as an idea or a concept, or as something only fixed for a moment for practical purposes." It is clear from this that, in Goethean terms, a living organism can only be conceived of as a *time-gestalt*. This, in turn, implies that *the whole organism is never physically manifest at any one time, as least as a rule*." (Suchantke, 2011, p.10)

This way of seeing—*looking with* rather than *looking at*—was one that shifted profoundly my experience of dandelion (Chapter 3). The plant realm is, alchemically, associated with the Element Water in many accounts, demonstrating (if we engage *with it* and not merely look *at it)* the constantly changing and metamorphosing process of growth and decay.

What may be apparent to a reader of Stafford's poem is that it is not just 'the world' that changes when we shift our way of seeing from an *Earthly* mode to a *Watery* mode, but *we too change* in the process. We shift from being self-centered and removed from our context or surroundings into a relational being who *participates* in a realm of becomings.

Ways of seeing—it's Elemental!

... this goodly frame, the
earth, seems to me a sterile promontory, this most
excellent canopy, the air, look you, this brave
o'erhanging firmament, this majestical roof fretted
with golden fire, why, it appears no other thing to
me than a foul and pestilent congregation of vapors.
What a piece of work is a man! how noble in reason!
how infinite in faculty! in form and moving how
express and admirable! in action how like an angel!
in apprehension how like a god! the beauty of the
world! the paragon of animals! And yet, to me,
what is this quintessence of dust?
        —William Shakespeare, *Hamlet, Act II, Scene 2*

In pointing to the other elements (Water, Air, and Fire) as being overlooked in a one-sidedly Earthly way of seeing, we find Steiner to be indicating different possibilities for *ways of seeing* or *disclosing* 'reality.' Viewed in this light, the science of the last few hundred years has been—dominantly—a science of the Earthly. The language that arises from this science roots us deeply in an Earthly mindscape.[82] This science has at

---

82. "We live in a dimension of mind which is as invisible to us as the air we breathe." Bortoft, see Chapter 2.

times made claims to be *the* justified approach to the science of nature (and the human being) rather than being *an* approach.[83] In its rightful domain, this *Earthly* way of seeing or mode of consciousness is of course totally justified.[84] When applied with carte blanche to the whole complexity of phenomena that we encounter, it gives rise to a radical reduction of that complexity to 'dust.'

Steiner clearly proposes that there are other ways of constituting our science (approaches to knowledge). We can infer from the above that there is, accepting this terminology for the time being, a *Watery* way, an *Airy* way, and a *Fiery* way (at the least).

Referring to a somewhat different, though related, proposal Henri Bortoft writes:

> This is a liberating step. It frees us from our enthrallment with the science which has been established, by making us aware that such a science does not have the absolute (i.e. self-standing) foundations that we customarily assume. Such a step makes us aware that in our scientific-technological world, or, more precisely, in the a priori presuppositions of this world, we have opted for one particular possibility, grounded in one particular situation. There could, therefore, be other possibilities.[85]

Dis-enchantment

> *We live in a world of meanings, though we are convinced that we live in a world of things.*
> — *Georg Kühlewind*

---

83. Consider the following statement by geometrician George Adams: "Occasionally, scientists of the Nineteenth Century—W.K. Clifford, for example—reflected that cosmic space might after all be 'non-Euclidean,' its structure differing from the Euclidean to so slight an extent as to escape our instruments of measurement. But neither this nor Einstein's four-dimensional space-time did more than modify the profoundly Euclidean—I might call it earthly—way of thinking about space and the realities it contains. This is so taken for granted as to be difficult to describe; few people realize that there is any other way." (Adams, 1989)

84. Steiner points to Goethe as having had, as the basis of his approach to science, a recognition of just this insight—that different phenomena invite different *ways of seeing* and that one task of the scientist is to accommodate to the phenomena rather than demand that all phenomena are revealed through one way of seeing.

85. (Bortoft, 1996, p. 322)

If we are to give due attention to Steiner's indication—"which cannot be taken seriously enough"—that we have neglected other possible modes of consciousness in our concerted attention to the *Earthly* mode then we can conceive of the following.

If our attention is to be placed on the mineral kingdom, which embodies to a large extent those dynamics 'cold' and 'dry,' we are right in choosing an Earthly way of seeing. If our attention is to be placed on a plant we can do so out of an attention to its physical manifestation before us and a consideration of its parts. This is to treat the plant as an Earth. We can, however, also 'plunge into perception' (Bortoft) and shift our attention to the plant as a 'grow-thing,' a verb or *becoming*,[86] and in doing so shift our attention to include the whole context in and out of which the plant emerges (which alchemically is to include the planetary realm, indicated through our considerations of water/fluids and their inherent responsiveness to moon and extra-terrestrial dynamics).

We can continue this path of enquiry to engage with the animal kingdom and a concurrent shift into a consideration of the warmth nature of *beings*[87] who are not only 'embodied' (Earth) and in constant becoming (Water) but who are also 'sensitive' or ensouled (Air). A consideration of an animal must, from this perspective, not just be done out of a way of seeing appropriate for a mineral, for only that aspect of the animal which is mineral-like will be revealed through such a lens (a tendency all too often played out in the science of our day—see discussion of the Enviropig in Chapter 3). Understanding *animal* invites us, in the context of the Four Elements, to develop ways of knowing appropriate or adequate to including the 'well nigh spiritual' elements of Air and Fire. We have entered the realm of the imponderables—and those aspects of living, ensouled, and spiritually endowed beings who *cannot* be understood or comprehended from a way of seeing that has reduced appearances to Earth-words.

---

86. As in my encounter with dandelion, Chapter 3.

87. The connection of warmth/heat with the intrinsic nature of different animals was described through my own experiences with alchemical research in Chapter 6. See reflections on 'hen' and 'dragon.'

We will, if we continue upon the path outlined thus far, arrive at the human being and the challenge of engaging with ways of seeing that are adequate to the unique nature of the human as a being who experiences self-consciousness, and has its own 'spark' of creative (or destructive!) genius—Fire.

Back to Biodynamics

These brief considerations reveal the following additional dimension to the creative 'spark' that lies behind the biodynamic preparations.

The synergies that emerged through a consideration of *sal* as a dynamic woven throughout the Oak Bark Preparation (Chapter 7) are enhanced through the choice of origin of the components of the preparation. The end point of the *coming into being* of calcium—limestone—is *not* chosen.[88] This is, elementally speaking, a 'cold' and 'dry' corpse, the final resting place of the activity of the calcic.

Instead, for 'enlivening' compost in a balanced manner, the preparation is availing itself of the vitalized *calcic* (verb) as expressed in the plant (a being of planetary dimension) and the *calcic* sensitized by the animal (a being of more-than-planetary dimension, a zodiacal being), 'seasoned' by the stimulation of the *calcic* process in the soil through the winter. All of this choreography arises through the intent of a human being who is working to activate calcium as a *dynamic* which can work sensitively and in harmony with other substance-activities (usually called 'elements') in the transformation of compost.

Calcium, as it is being 'activated' in the biodynamic preparation, emerges through a consideration of the Four Elements more akin to a 'note' or 'expression,' colored differently depending on its 'host' or instrument, and sounding in context with other notes in the creative music of substance.

Calcium is not just...well...calcium.

---

88. Lime is not used for the preparations. Steiner discusses using it in a compost heap directly, as is common practice, but the primary ingredients for the preparations, he advises, need to arise from the 'living realms,' and not from the mineral.

In Summary

In going to such lengths to reveal what the alchemical language *disclosed* I have taken the effort to illustrate that there is a world of difference between Water and water. The latter, for contemporary science, has been subjected to a deeply reductive and analytical way of seeing and its 'un-Earthly' properties either denied or, at best, tolerated as 'anomalies.'[89] This is the homogenization I referred to earlier, and which Steiner alludes to in his statement above—that science has become fundamentalist in adopting an Earthly way of seeing, and demanding that all phenomena are disclosed (prepared, even) through an Earthly lens and language. Whereas this is, of course, appropriate for that realm of phenomena which embody or reveal the qualities of 'coldness' and 'dryness' (particularly the case with the inorganic realms) a great error is made if this approach is applied full scale to *all phenomena,* even, or especially, to those which clearly reveal dynamics other than the static, self-contained nature of Earth. Such a reduction of *all phenomena* to be 'disclosed' through an Earthy lens results in a collapsing of the qualitative differentiation inherent in the word-nature of the Four Elements and gives rise to a uni-dimensional or homogenized science of distinction that sacrifices meaningful relation.

To re-engage with the alchemical worldview through the word-nature of the Four Elements and the Three Principles is to re-engage a timeless map or mandala which can re-orient our attention in its encounters with muck and with mind. These Elemental ways of seeing can form the basis for a renewed engagement with our encounters, both 'outwardly' and 'inwardly' contributing to a disenchantment of our science and agriculture from "the limits of a purely materialistic philosophy."[90]

∞

---

89. Consider, for example, the experience of Jacques Benveniste, whose research into what he termed *The Memory of Water* has been sidelined and denounced by the dominant scientific paradigm. See *The Memory of Water*, by Michel Schiff (1994).

90. The work of Dennis Klocek, referred to at various points in this book, exemplifies this potential for a renewed engagement with the Four Elements and the alchemical worldview, and his work in climatology, agriculture, personal development and consciousness studies is of far reaching importance in this regard. See *The Seer's Handbook,* and *Sacred Agriculture* as significant examples of this innovative approach to science.

The Water of Life

I have now distilled out four fractions of water and labelled them in separate bottles.

I am off to get some seeds to see how they will respond to these different (!) waters...Waters?

There certainly doesn't seem—visibly—to be any difference between them. All water, from that account.

It's got me thinking though. Water...the stuff of life...the great Mercury!

How bizarre that we think we can come to terms with it purely through analysis and a reduction of this wondrous liquid to its chemical constituents. As if it could just be explained by 'separating out' and classifying its building blocks.

Take these seeds for instance. Totally encased in dryness and hardness. Who can tell if one of these little packages isn't just a stone or grit of sand? Dead, lifeless...

And then, following the directions 'just add water'—'hey presto' a whole drama begins to unfold.

This is still a mystery in the best sense of the word. A mystery untouched by the science of the day. The great wonder that water plays as catalyst in the resurrection of the lifeless seed, in the sustenance of the living...

It's spring and life is, in fact, literally pouring forth out there... and its time to dive in...

Our weekend jaunts are now not canal-bound, but initiated with an early morning walk down the lane to Slad Farm. It is lambing time and the girls are eager to be a part of this seasonal renaissance of abundance. We head out in the morning, intending to help out for a few hours, and I don't see the girls for the rest of the day.

I too am swept up in it all and before long find myself chest deep in cows, and liberally scented with the sweet (?) smell of silage.

Sheep seem to have missed out on all the talk of entropy.

Just the other week it was a barn full of a portly thirty or so mothers with plenty of room to move, and now you can't walk in there for tripping over little uns' that are running around under foot. With two lambs apiece (or in the odd case three) that is a pretty decent increase of life by all accounts.

I'm thinking the word 'gambolling' must have been coined specifically for these little woolies or at least they have taken it to heart like few other critters. They have a surprising ability—and joy it seems—in jumping vertically..., yes straight UP from standing...no run at it...and no crouch down first either...just UP..before tearing off and around the barn doing more impossible leaps—gambols?—while on the trot.

This gravity-defying behavior is, no doubt, where we get the term 'spring' for this time of year...

Plants, it seems, also missed out on the wisdom of 'limited energy' and 'world running down' and all that. Each dandelion that finds its way into my garden (despite my attempts at weeding them out) can produce a staggering number of seeds in each clock and several clocks in a seasons' growth. Some say this profundity goes into the thousands—per plant—and there are a good few coming up in the garden, I can tell you.

One beech seed, given a rooting chance, can—in the course of its treeing lifetime—generate potential offspring that reach into the tens of thousands. If each one took, we'd be for it!...overwhelmed by biomass.

I am reminded of a passage in Pilgrim at Tinker Creek... *"The experimenters studied a single grass plant, winter rye. They let it grow in a greenhouse for four months; then they gingerly spirited away the soil...and counted and measured all the roots and hairs. In four months the plant had set forth 378 miles of roots—that's about three miles a day—in 14 million distinct roots. This is mighty impressive, but when they get down to the root hairs, I boggle completely. In those same four months the rye plant created 14 billion root hairs, and those little strands placed end-to-end just about wouldn't quit. In a single cubic inch of soil, the length of the root hairs totaled 6000 miles."*

And all of this made possible, midwifed in fact, by that miraculous fluid—water.

I really struggle to imagine that all this started from a random event in some kind of ancient petri-dish type of meeting between lifeless molecules. Life springing from the dead dust. And I am not alone in this doubt. Farmers deal with life on a daily basis and are in a good position to consider its mysteries. They are, it would seem, not all convinced by the proposal that all this gamboling is, at root, a mere accident. As Wendell Berry[91] put it:

91. from *Leavings*, Counterpoint, 2011

BY CHANCE,
OF COURSE

*WHILE ATTENDING THE ANNUAL CONVOCATION
OF CAUSE THEORISTS AND BIGBANGISTS AT THE
LOCAL PROVINCIAL RESEARCH UNIVERSITY, THE
MAD FARMER INTERCEDES FROM THE BACK ROW*

"Chance" is a poor word among
the mazes of causes and effects, the last
stand of these all-explainers who,
backed up to the first and final Why,
reply, "By chance, of course!" As if
that tied up ignorance with a ribbon.
In the beginning something by chance
existed that would bang and by chance
it banged, obedient to the by-chance
previously existing laws of existence
and banging, from which the rest proceeds
by logic of cause and effect also
previously existing by chance?

Ah well, it's spring, and I'll save the punch line of this piece for you to pursue. I have some seeds to plant…and it's time to dig up that yarrow prep.

Now, where did I put that haggis in the ground….?

10
Poïesis

"You don't ever let go of the thread."

William Stafford

"Nature's life and flow are so fine and subtle that in the end they slip right through the coarse mesh of our rational concepts. That's the mistake science has made in recent times—it tries to use coarse conceptual nets to catch things that are actually much too fine for them."

(Steiner, 1993, p. 56)

Recapitulation

I began this journey of encounters with a set of questions.

Initially I asked—is our culture healthy? Is our agriculture healthy?

The scene was set for seeking answers to these questions with two examples of 'solutions' developed to ameliorate symptoms of imbalance or loss of vitality in the agricultural domain. The path I have taken has focussed more on those intricacies of *consciousness* which are stimulated by an encounter with biodynamics than on the technicalities of *compost* preparations designed to enliven the latter. Culture and agriculture, from this perspective, are both expressions of a particular mode of consciousness or way of seeing. From the initial impetus of modified pigs and buried bark I have followed a thread through mind and matter, through muck and meaning to this point.

Thought-trails have woven through the fields of *epistemology* and *alchemy*, passing some dandelions along the way.

These forays have yielded some fruits.

This harvest includes considerations of the significance of *right separation* and *right synthesis* (Chapters 5 through 8), of the Tria Principia as a guiding principle for the making of distinctions without a loss of meaningful relations (Chapter 7) and of the importance of *language*, investigated through a consideration of the gulf between an element and the Elements—between water and Water (Chapter 9).

I can say now with some conviction that *health* continues to allude us in significant ways in terms of many of our cultural activities (I have focussed on science and agriculture in these musings). Arising out of a mode of consciousness that has backed itself into a corner or quadrant—the Earthly—and denied or neglected the other three (Water, Air and Fire), our agri-culture is guided by forces that are self-centered, piecemeal, and all too ready to accept solutions that arise from the manipulation of parts which have been denied their relation to the whole.

The Enviropig stands as just one example of the type of creation that emerges, and will continue to emerge, from a consciousness that continues to manipulate *parts* in an attempt to solve its self-sown mistakes. The alternative which is offered in the encounters I have considered is that we should stop tweaking the pig (or plant, or fish, or fowl...) and step into those quadrants which we have neglected. This bold but necessary step would be a recognition that it is *we who need to change*, and not the four-footed, finned or flowered ones who are in our care.

These strands will now be taken up in a final consideration of what lies as potential in the biodynamic approach to the cultivation of new compost, of new consciousness and of a renewed agri-culture.

A poetics of substance

I have come to see the creation of the biodynamic preparations in terms of *poïesis*. I use this term in the sense of "an action that transforms and continues the world."[92] Such an act is described as "neither technical production nor creation in the romantic sense, *poïetic* work reconciles thought with matter and time, and person with the world."

In choosing this way of framing the creations called biodynamic preparations I am very conscious of shifting an emphasis away from 'scientific' explanations, where 'science' still means reduction, quantification, abstract representation, and removal of the scientist (the 'knower') from the process of knowledge. In proposing this shift I am very aware that such a proposal (i.e. that *poïesis* lies at the heart of biodynamics)

---

92. www.poiesisfoundation.org/

may be wholly unsatisfactory to this same science—poetry is thin on statistics. Quantitative proofs that biodynamic preparations *work* (or not) aren't—from this point of view—going to come from the poetic mind.[93]

However I suggest that the *poïesis* of preparation-making arises from a gesture in consciousness which overcomes the habit of homogenization and reduction—the tendency to reduce all encounters to a singular lens and 'way of seeing'—and seeks, instead, to attune *itself*, accommodate itself to the mode of that which it encounters. The biodynamic preparations furthermore arise out of an attunement to *context,* and this attunement is a reconciliation of those aspects of the preparations which are held, in conventional approaches to science and agriculture, as separate and therefore of negligible consequence. Considerations of the significance of time, place, origin of materials, intention of the maker, and attitude toward the effect of the preparations moves them from the realm of mere 'additives' in a mechanistic or material sense (i.e., in order to increase production) toward elements of a creative performance, an act that 'furthers the world.' In this way the preparations are akin to artistic creations, but creations derived from an Art which *encompasses* the rigor of science, of aesthetic sensitivity and a sense for the sacred role of land stewardship.

This Art can be called *alchemical* in that it recognizes the *solve et coagula* of consciousness, the polar activities of the intellect, and an imaginative consciousness that both separates and recombines with due consideration to the participatory role that lies as potential for the human being in our interactions with nature. It is *alchemical* in that it is multi-perspectival, aware of the dangers of a single lens or way of knowing, and embracing, instead, a complex responsiveness to a dynamic world. The Art of biodynamics is, furthermore, alchemical in that it is rooted in the recognition of a mutually transformative process whereby the human being and the Earth are both changed in the dialog between soul and soil, between muck and mind.

---

93. Quantitative proofs can, of course, be applied to those aspects of phenomena which are quantifiable. The point being made here is that those aspects cultivated by the biodynamic farmer or gardener—vitality and resilience—are not readily quantifiable. Biodynamic researchers have thus developed a range of methods for qualitative assessment of produce grown with these methods.

Returning to considerations of the *paradigm* of biodynamics considered in Chapter 2, the perspective that I am offering is that biodynamics presents one (of several) instances of a potential paradigm shift in our cultural activities, not only in our agri-culture but also in our science, art, and spiritual life. Considered *alchemically*, these are inseparable. The biodynamic preparations represent potent instances of how such a paradigm shift manifests in practical life, though they are essentially a creation of a transformed inner life. The current cultural paradigm, still deeply enamored with reductionist, mechanistic and materialistic perspectives, will not embrace these preparations readily[94] as such a shift requires considerable attention and openness to new ways of seeing, doing and being.

Preparations

All these elements are inwardly related to a very specifically differentiated spirituality. They are quite different than the elements modern chemistry talks about. Modern chemistry talks only about the corpses of substances, not about the real substances. We have to get to know their living, sensitive aspect.
(Steiner, 1993, p. 54)

I have chosen to sprinkle the works of poets like seeds throughout this book for the very reason that I see the poet as a figure throughout history who both *guides* and *bridges*—whose Art is to both distinguish and to relate, separate and recombine but more than any other act or offer, the poetic mind is sensitive in *reconciling* matter, time, person, and world. Poetry arises from a 'spontaneous sober observation of the world,' a rigorous attention that is deeply engaged in the 'stuff' of the world, but without denying its resonance with the mind and heart of the observer. The poetic mind seeks in its science and art to attune to the Word-nature of the encounter—be it a stone or plant, pig or bark, a dragon

---

94. As with studies in homeopathy and 'the memory of water,' the preparations are likely to be denounced and denied validity even as the body of research into their efficacy grows. This is to be expected in the face of a scientific community which still censors and rejects any area of research that does not fit neatly into its methodology and accepted ideology. Once again Michel Schiff's *The Memory of Water* is worthy of note for its examination of the issue of censorship in science.

or a hen—seeking to know not only the noun-ness or corpse of the other, but its *becoming*, its responding and its Being. Any encounter, in this light, is a meeting, a mutual moment—and not a manipulation. The biodynamic oak bark preparation, as poïetic *offering*, arises from an understanding of the Word-nature of calcium, the *calcic*, an affordance that is not limited to its material boundary or bonds. The activity of calcium is *sal*—an activity that reconciles Earth and Water. Taker of shapes, a builder of bridges, from fluid to fixed, the holder of form. Rind of oak, shell of egg, scaffold of bone, life bearer and barrier, both in one, calcium is dynamically different depending on how it is 'hosted'.[95]

As in the spagyric remedy, the Oak Bark preparation comes about through a 'solve et coagula' that enhances the calcic principle ('two-hundredthfold') in the transformation of compost as a bearer of 'new being.' This coagula unfolds in the vessel of the earth, circulated through the rhythms of the winter sun, moon and stars—an exalted substance to serve in the great transformation of the garden and grower, the human and the humus.

∞

Essence

The biodynamic preparations emerge as creative offerings arising from an exact imaginative discipline in science and a sense for the informing qualities of time and place, the preparations situate the one who makes and uses them back into the uniqueness of local domains, reconciling the rift that has arisen through an abstract, objective stance derived from a consciousness of 'dust and ashes'.[96]

The preparations *prepare* both the compost and its creator for another round in the cycle of life. This is an act of service that arises from an ontology that recognizes *life* as primary, and that matter which is all

---

95. "For the calcium to have a healing effect, however, it has to be calcium from something living, we cannot evade the organic realm. It won't help at all to add ordinary lime or any other calcium compound that has fallen out of the organic realm" (Steiner, 1993, p.101).

96. New preparations made by Dennis Klocek, Hugo Erbe, Glen Atkinson, Enzo Nastati and others are examples of how the biodynamic approach to land stewardship is both individualized and localized as well as in constant development and adaptation to local conditions and events.

too often taken as the basis for all of life as *derivative*, a precipitate which has separated out (solve) of living process.[97]

The essence that emerges from the alchemical perspective explored above—for the learner, teacher, and researcher of Biodynamics—is that in this new direction for stewardship of the land a radical re-orientation of knowing, responding, and doing emerges. These three faculties, distinct yet intrinsically related, require a conscious repositioning by the practitioner, teacher, or researcher such that human activity finds a place once again within a meaningful field of reciprocal relations. Rather than unfolding our interactions with the substances and beings of nature as 'commands' or 'demands' we can participate in a mutually enhancing dialogue.

This realization completes the circle: "Every way of knowing becomes a way of living, every epistemology becomes an ethic."

The Stones

…I broke them where they slugged in their dark
cells, and lifted them up in pieces.
As I piled them in the light
I began their music. I heard their old lime
rouse in breath of song that has not left me…
> Wendell Berry[98]

---

97. "The substance you are potentizing was originally formed from the cosmic periphery inward, by an individually rhythmic, not to say musical, relation between the cosmic periphery and the earthly centre. True, it has come to rest in the earthly place where it abides—in root or leaf of plant, in metal or crystal, mineral, or even in the bottle on the apothecar's shelves. But this is only its last resting place. In the precise earthly locality where it was first precipitated, it came into being through a specific and individual relation between the earth-planet and the vast spheres of the cosmos. In this relation lies the secret of its chemical individuality qua substance, and its vital nature if still embedded in the living realm. The formative rhythm is still latent in it, and when the careful hand of the pharmacist… subjects it to the rhythmic process of expansion, mingling it by trituration or succussion with the spatial medium which is to receive it, an opportunity is given for the formative rhythm of its origin to be re-born and for its latent connection with the healing essences of the cosmos to be restored…Is not the picture I have been giving in harmony with Hanemann's own words quoted above, when he speaks of the spirit-like individuality of the substance which in the crude material lies latent and concealed?" (Adams, 1961, p. 6)

98. from *The Selected Poems of Wendell Berry*, Counterpoint, 1998.

I'm heading back to the workshop.

I am on the trail of 'warmth' again, this time following Hugo Erbe's lead.

This spring I am going to have to hand a 'warmth preparation,' just in case… in case we have another one like we did in 2012.

The spring of 2012 was a strange one. At first, things went as expected.

Air temperatures rose, days grew longer and brighter…a springy spring.

It was a year that I decided to sketch the apple buds as they unfolded on the tree behind the house. Every day or so I would go out and draw the next stage of unfolding, building up a sequence of images of the 'becoming of apple.' It all went fine. I was there with Ergemont Russet right through bud-break, the opening of the blossoms…

Then, virtually overnight, it all stopped.

A cold cycle set up with frigid air dropping down out of the north.

Day upon day I would go out with pad and pencil and nothing had happened. Freeze frame.

The wicked witch of the north had cast her spell and the princess was asleep, along with the rest of the court—not least the bees.

It was too cold for the pollinators to fly and the expectant apple blossoms waited in vain for a visit from one of those winged wonders.

There was a massive reduction in the apple crop that year across the whole of Gloucestershire.

So, you might imagine my curiosity when I came upon this mix in the work of Hugo Erbe[99] *for* "the prevention of damage from early and late frosts" (prep 1) *and* "to counter a lack of warmth during the summer growing season" (prep 2).

I decided to try these out, figuring that I might learn something from a man whose profound knowledge of gardening and nutrition led him to develop new strains of spelt, wheat, and other grains which far exceeded the yield and quality of other grains grown at the time (or grown today).

He was, I think, working with a profoundly alchemical understanding of substance and process.

And so to the lab…and to prepare the ingredients…

---

99. Hugo Erbe's *New Biodynamic Preparations*, available from www.considera.org.

Pine charcoal, honey, formic acid, pine resin, egg white, brandy...

I have myself an old biscuit tin, and have liberally dotted the top with holes hammered in with a nail. I have filled the tin with pine branches and twigs. The tin, tied shut with a wire, is quickly slipped atop a burning pile of wood in the wood burner in the living room and then the door closed.

It is quite a treat to watch the process through the wood stoves' window, the biscuit tin producing a candelabra of flame as the charcoaling process unfolds.

Back in the workshop the charcoal dust starts to get everywhere as I grind it, first in a meat grinder and then in a mortar and pestle.

I have some pine resin that I collected last time I was at the lake in Ontario, and it exudes a rich aroma that instantly transports me back to sun-sparkled water, granite banks cleft with pine roots, trunks stretching high into cloud dappled sky. It is as if all that summer sunshine and sticky heat that is only bearable when living at lakeside has been packed or distilled into this golden, translucent resin. An exudation of warmth-wrought sap.

As I compose with these ingredients from plant and animal kingdoms I ponder the life and mind of this prep's creator. Erbe was a remarkable man and he led a life still largely unknown and un-acknowledged. His awareness and devotion to the Beings that stand behind the 'wrought works' of Nature is humbling and makes me all too aware of the clunkiness of my own thinking and way of seeing.

Arms blackened in charcoal, the room filling with a heady mix of honey and brandy, I am filled with that exhilarating, and yet also slightly disconcerting sense, that there is still so, so much to learn...

Post Script

I have come to the conclusion that a vast potential is presented in the biodynamic approach to land stewardship that will, however, only be fully realized through a process that addresses the transformation or metamorphosis of the practitioner along with the development of new practices and new techniques. Viewed from this perspective the biodynamic preparations are both functional agents for transforming the soil, the earth, and the plants as well as being seeds for the transformation of consciousness itself.

In this study, a contribution toward this mutual transformation is explored through a series of encounters with preparation making and a journey into the alchemical world. Alchemical processes, images, theory, and practice lead me to conclude that one of the most potent possibilities that lies in this way of seeing/knowing is in the invitation to move from a binary, dualistic way of knowing—that continues to shape so much of our contemporary culture—to a re-engagement with processes unfolding as dynamic polarities.

The Four Elements and Three Principles articulate polar relationships which cannot be easily grasped by the 'either/or' tendencies of the intellectual mind. Through a cultivation of an imaginative way of knowing, the possibility is opened toward working with the creative tension that is ever at play in the dance of polarities (forming/dissolving, expanding/contracting...) and the paradoxes that arise when these polar dynamics inform the realms of life and living systems.[100] Biodynamics embraces these polarities (and paradoxes) by re-engaging with the two-fold—cosmos and earth, levity and gravity, light and dark, warm and cold—while also emphasizing the mediating activity of a third principle. Though not reducible to one simple example,

---

100. "Polarity does not try to take opposition away. Mind and matter, man and nature, conscious and unconscious, subject and object—all remain apart, in tension. We don't ultimately choose one of the contraries over the other or bring them together at last in a climactic embrace or fusion. Any 'resolution of opposites' would mean the disappearance of one through its engulfment by the other, or else a denial of the original opposition through some philosophical or verbal sleight-of-hand. " Cover notes to *Evolution of Consciousness: Studies in Polarity*

this mediating, *mercur* principle is potently evident in the biodynamic method in the recognition of the role of the human being in the unfolding and 'furthering' of world process. For it is the human being, as *participant,* who can re-establish a field of relations between the seemingly distinct realms of plant and planet, season and substance, self and other. This amounts to a *poïesis,* a shift from mere management to sensitive stewardship. It is to build a bridge between the sal of science and the sulf, or soul, of the beings who populate our farms and gardens with the mercur of heartfelt-knowing. It is a very precise activity that is asked of us but "precise in the way a poem is precise not in the way a formula is precise."[101] This, in my experience as gardener and teacher, is not an easy task; it is a very far-reaching poïesis that is proposed. As a contribution to this task, however, I have found that a renewed attention to the Art of separating and recombining—the three-in-one—has shown itself to be an effective way of knowing for these initial steps towards understanding, learning, and practicing Biodynamics.

---

101. Klocek, 2009.

The Way It Is

by William Stafford

There's a thread you follow. It goes among
things that change. But it doesn't change.
People wonder about what you are pursuing.
You have to explain about the thread.
But it is hard for others to see.
While you hold it you can't get lost.
Tragedies happen; people get hurt
or die; and you suffer and get old.
Nothing you do can stop time's unfolding.
You don't ever let go of the thread.

An Offer of Praise

for W. Berry and W. Stafford

Farmers are well placed.
Poets place themselves well.
Both places and wells
      sustain
farmers and poets.
Poets and farmers
      maintain
places and wells.
Wellness declines if
farmers and poets become
displaced.
Places decline if
poets and farmers become
unwell-ed.
Let us give
praise to farmers,
      places,
      wells,
      and poets!

JMC, July 2014

Cited Works and Suggested Reading

Adams, George, "Potentization and the Peripheral Forces of Nature." Retrieved from http://www.anthromed.org/Article.aspx?artpk=710

Adams, George and Oliver Whicher, *The Plant Between Sun and Earth*. London: Rudolf Steiner Press, 1980

Allison John, *A Way of Seeing. Perception, Imagination and Poetry*. Great Barrington: Lindisfarne, 2003.

Barfield, Owen, *Worlds Apart: A Dialogue of the 1960s*. London: The Barfield Press, 2006

Bartlett, Robert Allen, *Real Alchemy*. Quinquangle Press, 2006.

Benesch, Friedrich and Klaus Wilde, *Silica, Calcium and Clay: Processes in Mineral, Plant, Animal and Man*. Illinois: Schaumburg Publications Inc., 1995.

Berry, Wendell, *It All Turns on Affection*. Berkeley, CA: Counterpoint, 2012.

Berry, Wendell, *Leavings*. Berkeley: Counterpoint, 2011.

Berry, Wendell, *The Selected Poems of Wendell Berry*. Berkeley: Counterpoint, 1998.

Berry, Wendell, *This Day: Collected and New Sabbath Poems*. Berkeley: Counterpoint, 2013.

Bortoft, Henry, *The Wholeness of Nature; Goethe's Way Toward a Conscious Participation in Nature*. New York, Lindisfarne Press, 1996.

Bortoft, Henry, *Taking Appearance Seriously: The Dynamic Way of Seeing in Goethe and European Thought*. Edinburgh: Floris Books, 2008.

Brady, R., Georg Maier and Stephen Edelglass, *Being on Earth: Practice In Tending the Appearances*, 2008

Burt, E.A., *The Metaphysical Foundations of Modern Science*. New York: Dover Publications, 2003.

Dillard, Annie, *Pilgrim at Tinker Creek*. New York, Harper Collins, 1974.

Einstein, Albert, "Foreword." in *Concepts of Space; The History of Theories of Space in Physics* by Max Jammer. Cambridge, MA: Harvard UP, 1969.

Erbe, Hugo, (2008) *New Biodynamic Preparations*. Mark Moodie Publications.

Forshaw, Peter, (2005) *Alchemy in the Amphitheatre: Some Considerations of the Alchemical Content of the Engravings in Heinrich Khunrath's Amphiteatre of Eternal Wisdom*. PhD Dissertation

Geldard, Richard, (2000) *Remembering Heraclitus*. New York: Lindisfarne Books.

Goethe, J.W.v, *Faust*. Trans. Walter Arndt, New York: Norton.

Goodrick-Clarke, Nicholas, *Paracelsus:Essential Readings*. Berkley, CA: North Atlantic Books, 1999.

Hauschka, Rudolf, *The Nature of Substance*. Sussex, Sophia Books, 2002.

Holdrege, Craig, *Thinking Like a Plant*. Great Barrington, MA: Lindisfarne Books, 2013.

Holdrege, Craig, "The Gene: A Needed Revolution." *In Context* #14 (Fall, 2005, pp. 14-17).

Jammer, Max, *Concepts of Space; The History of Theories of Space in Physics*. Dover,1993.

Jammer, Max, *Einstein and Religion: Physics and Theology*. Princeton UP, 2002.

Julius, Fritz, *Fundamentals for a Phenomenological Study of Chemistry*. Fair Oaks, CA: AWSNA Publications, 2000.

Junius, Manfred, *Spagyrics: The Alchemical Preparation of Medicinal Essences, Tinctures and Elixirs*. Vermont: Healing Arts Press, 2007.

Klocek, Dennis, *Seeking Spirit Vision*. Fair Oaks, CA: Rudolf Steiner College Press,1998.

Klocek, Dennis, *The Seer's Handbook*. Great Barrington, MA:SteinerBooks, 2005.

Klocek, Dennis, *Sacred Agriculture: The Alchemy of Biodynamics*. Great Barrington, MA: Lindisfarne Press, 2013.

Kuhlewind, Georg, *From Normal to Healthy*. Great Barrington, MA: Lindisfarne Press, 1988.

Kuhlewind, Georg, *The Light of the 'I': Guidelines for Meditation*. Great Barrington, MA: Lindisfarne Press, 2008.

Lehrs, Ernst, *Man or Matter*. London: Rudolf Steiner Press, 1985.

Lorand, Andrew, *Biodynamic Agriculture: A paradigmatic analysis,* PhD Thesis Pennsylvania State University, 1996.

Marti, Ernst, *The Four Ethers*. Schaumberg, Publications, 1984.

McGilchrist, Iain. *The Master and his Emissary: The Divided Brain and the Making of the Western World*. New Haven, CT:Yale UP, 2012.

Nemerov, Howard, *The Collected Poems of Howard Nemerov*. University of Chicago Press, 1981.

Palmer, Parker, (1993). *The violence of our knowledge: Toward a Spirituality of higher education*. Retrieved 11/15/09, from http://www.21learn.org/arch/articles/palmer_spirituality.html.

Pelikan, Wilhelm, *Healing Plants*. New York: Mercury Press, 1988.

Principe, Lawrence M, *The Secrets of Alchemy*. University of Chicago Press, 2013.

Read, John, *From Alchemy to Chemistry*. New York: Dover, 1995.

Rohen, Johannes, *Functional Morphology: The Dynamic Wholeness of the Human Organism*. Hillsdale, NY: Adonis Press, 2007.

Rohen, Johannes, *Functional Threefoldness in the Human Organism and Human Society*. Hillsdale, NY: Adonis Press, 2011.

Roob, A., *Alchemy and Mysticism*. Koln: Taschen, 2001.

Schad, Wolfgang, *Man and Mammal*. New York: The Waldorf Press, 1977.

Schiff, Michael, *The Memory of Water*. London: Thorsons/Harper Collins, 1994.

Shakespeare, W., *Hamlet*. Hertfordshire: Wordsworth Editions Ltd, 2002.

Shakespeare, W., *Macbeth*. Hertfordshire: Wordsworth Editions Ltd, 2002.

Stafford, William, *Ask Me: 100 Essential Poems*. Minneapolis: Graywolf, 2013.

Stafford, William, *Even in Quiet Places*. Winchester, ID: Confluence, 2010.

Steiner, Rudolf, *Alchemy: The Evolution of the Mysteries*. Rudolf Steiner Press, 2001.

Steiner, Rudolf, *Agriculture*. Kimberton, PA: Biodynamic Farming and Gardening Association, 1993.

Steiner, Rudolf, *The Four Seasons and the Archangels*. Forest Row, Sussex: Rudolf Steiner Press, 1996.

Steiner, Rudolf, *A Theory of Knowledge Implicit in Goethe's World Conception*. NY: Mercury Press, 1996.

Steiner, Rudolf, *Therapeutic Insights, Earthly and Cosmic Laws*. New York: Mercury Press, 1984.

Steiner, Rudolf, *Warmth Course*. New York: Mercury Press.

Storl, Wolf D., *Culture and Horticulture*. Bio-dynamic Literature, 1979.

Suchantke, Andreas, *Metamorphosis: Evolution In Action*. Hillsdale, NY: Adonis Press, 2011.

Sugerman, S. Ed., *Evolution of Consciousness: Studies in Polarity*. San Rafael, CA: Barfield Press, 1976.

Thornton Smith, Richard, *Cosmos, Earth and Nutrition: The Biodynamic Approach to Agriculture*. Forest Row, Sussex: Sophia Books, 2009.

Twentyman, Ralph, *The Science and Art of Healing*. Edinburgh: Floris Books, 1992.

Zajonc, Arthur (2006) *Love and Knowledge: Recovering the heart through Contemplation*. Teachers College Record. 108 (9), 1742-1759.

About the Author and Illustrator

JONATHAN CODE lives with his wife and two daughters in Stroud, UK where he cultivates a garden and undertakes research. He is the Senior Education and Research Coordinator of the Higher Education Department of Crossfields Institute and has taught practical chemistry, phenomenology, and nature study to learners of all ages for many years,.

ED BERGER is a biodynamic farmer and teacher at Vale Head Farm, a small mixed farm in Staffordshire, England, owned and operated by Ruskin Mill Trust. He has been involved in socially orientated biodynamic farming and growing for 15 years but previously studied art and design, focussing on furniture design and sculpture. Ed sees drawing as a means to engage and learn from the world, a way to drop ones expectations and really observe; an invaluable skill in illustrating, as well as teaching and farming. He lives on the farm with his partner, their two young children, and two dogs.

CPSIA information can be obtained at www.ICGtesting.com
Printed in the USA
BVOW05s0337300115

385629BV00003B/190/P